Pineapple Sundays

Bitter sweet tales of growing up in Swansea

First published in Great Britain in 2008 by
Bryngold Books Ltd.,
Golden Oaks, 98 Brynau Wood, Cimla,
Neath, South Wales, SA11 3YQ.
www.bryngoldbooks.com

Typesetting, layout, editing
and design
by Bryngold Books

ISBN 978-1-905900-04-6

Printed and bound
in Wales by
Gomer Press
Llandysul, Ceredigion.

Pineapple Sundays

Bitter sweet tales of growing up in Swansea

By Haydn Williams

BRYNGOLD
BOOKS

CONTENTS

CONTENTS

DEDICATION

For my darling wife Jean.

Also by the same author

Angels in Hobnail Boots
A wartime prequel to the stories
in this book and available from
Bryngold Books Ltd.
01639 643961,
bryngold@btinternet.com, or
www.bryngoldbooks.com

CHAPTER 1

Tom the car and the Tarzan sandwich

As a greeting the words were nothing out of the ordinary, but I knew instantly from the breathless urgency with which my best pal was delivering them that they held the promise of an exciting adventure though as yet there was no clue as to exactly what that could be.

"Hello, Mrs Swain, is Andy in? I gotta see him. Quick like." The words were like an early warning as they drifted into the house. They had been aimed at Mammy who was outside, pegging clothes on the line. I knew who it was instantly, I recognised the voice and I knew that the next second Dinky Miles, who always called me Andy even though my name was Handel, would come barging into the kitchen where I was breakfasting on bread and jam washed down with a cup of tea. He wouldn't bother to wait for Mammy to answer or even acknowledge him – he treated our house like his own.

Dinky could never just talk or say anything quietly. He had to shout as if it was some way of compensating for his diminutive stature, something that was confirmed by the noisy way he finally delivered his news.

"Andy! Come on – quick mun – outside. There's a car. Some men are pushing a car up the 'ill. You gotta come an' see it mun."

He was puffing and panting, jumping from one leg to the other and waving his arms all over the place. He was wearing a well-washed, red jersey, black shorts below his knees and the mandatory hobnail boots. His small stature meant that Dinky always had problems with clothes, particularly trousers. His face was lit up, his cheeks glowing red with a bright soapy shine. It was a Saturday morning sparkle that would become grubbier as the adventures of the day left their mark.

Men pushing a car! This was big news. Dinky was in a hurry to share it with me and by now he was tugging at my arm as he followed his initial outburst with: "Where they taking it, Andy mun?" I was ten, a full year older than Dinky and because of this he thought that I knew everything.

It was the spring of 1946 and the war had been over for nearly a year. Life seemed to have become mundane after the euphoria and great rejoicing of the previous year when the air seemed to be constantly filled with the salutes of victory over Germany and Japan. Now it seemed that the nation had slipped into a state of limbo. We were told – and believed – that things were going to get much better now that the war was over.

By now men were returning from the war in their droves. There was plenty of work for them instead of the dreaded dole which many had faced before they had gone off to war, but in some respects things got worse. Food rationing was still in force and bread and potatoes, plentiful during the worst years of the war, were now strangely scarce.

We even lacked the excitement of the latter years of the war which brought events like the arrival of the Americans in Swansea, the D-Day landings and victories over the enemy to brighten our lives. Worse still, now that Dinky's father was back home, there was a stricter discipline in the Miles' household. Little boys had to remain seen but not heard and their friends were no longer welcome, at least not when Mr Miles was at home. As a result my only access to a wireless had been lost. This meant Dinky and I could no longer share the adventures of classic BBC serials along with the light entertainment shows such as ITMA and Variety Bandbox that we also enjoyed listening to. There was a glimmer of hope though. We were holding our breath in anticipation after Mammy had hinted that, with my sisters Maggie and Molly now working, our household might soon have its own wireless.

For the moment however, Dinky was still tugging at my arm trying to pull me away from the table while I clutched an inch thick slice of bread and jam. Suddenly he stopped, momentarily forgetting about the men pushing the car. Instead he fixed his eyes on my breakfast. He thrust his head forward, his nose almost resting on my bread and jam.

"Give us a bite mun, Andy," he hollered before opening his mouth as wide as he possibly could. I didn't hesitate. I held out the bread and jam and soon there was a gaping, crescent-shaped chunk missing from one corner. It lasted in his mouth for all of two seconds before it was eagerly swallowed. This was normal. We had readily shared everything since our first meeting in an air raid shelter five years before. If he was eating an apple when we met up, without hesitation it would be thrust towards my mouth with the generous invitation to take a good bite. The same would apply to Welsh cakes or biscuits and if one of us was sucking a hard boiled sweet it would be cracked in two and a portion shoved into the other's mouth. We were pals.

Soon, with me clutching the remains of my bread and jam and Dinky bubbling with excitement, we were rushing through the back door – for some reason we never used the front. As we tore past Mammy, still pegging out clothes, she shouted a warning.

"Handel! Mind you now, don't be late for dinner."

"I won't be, Mammy," I shouted back. Her words were unnecessary. I wouldn't miss Saturday dinner for anything. My oldest brother Daniel had gone to Swansea market as usual and it would be fried cockles and laverbread on the table today.

"There they are Andy – I told you didn't I?" Dinky said triumphantly as we reached the road where the two men pushing the car had now been joined by four boys. They were older than us – thirteen or fourteen perhaps – and among them was my brother Harry. One of the men, who turned out to be the owner, had his hand through the open window of the driver's door, his fingers curled around the steering wheel. He wore a dark blue pinstripe suit which could have been described as smart once, but which looked baggy and grubby now through being worn to work. It was probably his demob suit. Lots of men were wearing these ill-fitting suits. There was another man on the other side of the car with the boys pushing at the back. It seemed hard work and their bodies were straining to keep the vehicle moving and on course, a task hampered by the fact that it was completely rusted up and its tyres were flat.

Eventually the car and the exhausted group reached the brow of the hill where the road widened and levelled out into Hafod Square. Here it seemed they believed the worst was over. Me and Dinky were standing on the road just outside my house watching them from a safe distance as they took a welcome breather from their strenuous efforts. Like Dinky, I wondered where they were going with the car.

After the group had rested for a while the proceedings got underway again. Moving the car was easier now as it was on a slight downward slope. As they came alongside us they came to a halt once more. The man steering took his hand off the wheel and joined his mate in front of the car. They were looking towards a row of five corrugated metal garages that stood in front of the Great Tip. The four older boys stayed at the back of the car with their hands on hips trying their best to look grown-up and important.

The men were alongside a wide gap in the bank which had been carved out by Sergeant Nick, a bulldozer-driving American soldier, during the war to allow easier access to the tip for the big Yankee trucks. The slope to get on to the land where the garages stood was not that steep and if the car had power there wouldn't have been a problem in moving it to its final destination. By now I assumed this would be one of the garages, two of which were already in use – one on an almost daily basis by Mrs James who kept a grocer's shop on the main road and the one where my brother Harry had broken a window two years earlier and landed up in the Juvenile Court.

After deliberating for a few minutes the men decided that there was nothing for it but to fill in some of the larger potholes on the roughly hewn track and, with the help of the boys, put their backs into shoving the car once more. Before they started, Harry shouted across to us.

"Keep away from 'ere 'andel, it's dangerous. You too, Dinky," he said with his chest puffed up to match his ego.

Neither of us intended doing anything other than keeping away. The only thing really dangerous there was Harry, but from past experience we knew better than to answer him back. Harry could be mean and vindictive. Anyway it was much more fun watching from a distance as the car, which they had started to push once more, seemed an awkward beast to handle.

For the first few yards they were helped by the slight gradient of the road. Harry and his pals, pushing at the back, decided to use this advantage by taking a run at it, with Harry shouting: "Right boys, push and run!" It seemed to work and the car gathered momentum. The trouble was that the man with his hand on the steering wheel couldn't turn it quickly enough because of the vehicle's flat tyres and he ended up bellowing "Stop you bloody fools! Stop!"

He struggled to turn the steering wheel while at the same time dragging his heels on the ground in a bid to slow the vehicle down. Worse still, the man on the other side was running so close to the front wheel that, as it turned, his boot was caught under the flat tyre. With the side of the car gradually bearing down on him he was on his knees before he finally managed to drag himself clear, by which time he was adding to the mayhem by cursing and shouting.

"You cowin' stupid idiots! Trying to cowin' kill me," he screamed. With that the boys stopped pushing and backed away from the car, visibly scared by his anger. Two of them – Harry I must admit wasn't one – were already doing a runner not knowing how the men would react, particularly the one on the ground who was now cradling his injured leg in his arms.

"Oh dear God! Iesu Annwyl. They've broken my cowin' leg mun," he moaned. From his cursing I could tell that his first language was Welsh. I had heard 'Iesu Annwyl' often enough from my Welsh-speaking mother when she was in a temper. The car was now in the worst possible position, slewed at an angle, half on the road and half on the gravel path. The man who had been steering went to see how badly injured his companion was. Although obviously in pain he was soon up on his feet shaking his fist and still swearing at the boys who were, for the moment at least, keeping a safe distance. I could understand their reasoning for keeping clear of the men until their tempers had cooled a little. In the event this took all of a few minutes of foot-stamping and furious leg rubbing by the injured man. Then after some words of encouragement from the car's owner whose sole aim was to get it safely up to the garage, he was soon calling the boys back.

"All right boys, come on. No harm done is it, we still need your help," he cajoled.

They needed little encouragement and came running back to the car eager to resume the action as the man steering shouted some instructions.

"Right boys, let's straighten her up first – then we can get a good run at it," he said.

His mate, believing the boys to be a malicious bunch of hooligans, chipped in with "And try not to cowin' kill me this time. Right!"

The first part of the operation went smoothly. They reversed the car back out into the middle of the road, lined the front wheels up to the ash and clinker path then, with a man each side and the boys yelling at the back, they ran the car at the gradient. They got up a good speed and did it in one go, but not in the way I expected. As the car left the road and hit the ash and clinker surface it bounced into the air. The boys pushing at the back let go as the momentum took the car forward. The job was done, but the car was now minus one of its front wheels. Unfortunately the men, who hadn't let go, were now sprawled on the ground. This time both of them were writhing and cursing.

Harry and his mates didn't hang around this time. Instead they were haring for the park as fast as their legs could carry them. Me and Dinky turned and scooted back to the refuge of my house from where we watched the men as they picked themselves up. The car's owner was leaning on the bonnet looking down and inspecting the damage to the wheels. His mate had given up and was already hobbling back down Pentremawr Hill. We watched as the owner of the car tinkered with it for a while, opening the doors, lifting the bonnet and boot lid.

Eventually he gave the wheels a kick before he too walked off. The morning's excitement was over.

Before long Daniel returned from the market with the laverbread and cockles for our dinner. As a family we thought laverbread – black seaweed chopped up into a thick paste – was delicious, though for some the mere sight of it was revolting. Harry, trying to put me off eating it said it reminded him of the cowpats in the fields of our uncle's farm. That didn't work with me, Walter or Eddie as we'd been weaned on the stuff, but in the past Harry had succeeded in putting off Dinky from savouring laverbread. Until today that was.

Dinky had decided that he was having dinner with us – bread and cockles – but no laverbread. Molly, my sister, had also arrived home. Saturday was her half-day from work and she was helping Mammy with the dinner. She had already cooked four slices of thick, salty Welsh bacon which was on a plate in the top oven keeping warm. Next into the frying pan, spitting and fizzing, went a mountain of fat, juicy, shelled cockles. Mammy tossed and mixed them into the sizzling bacon fat, sweating and slightly crisping them before quickly spooning them into a large dish which she placed with the bacon in the oven. She then scooped the laverbread which had been rolled in oatmeal, out of its greaseproof paper and into the remaining bacon fat which had now taken on the flavour of the cockles.

Saturday dinner was a mouth-watering experience when the house was filled with the mixed aromas of the strong Welsh bacon, the tangy cockles and the delicate laverbread. It was like a magic lure. The only person missing from the table was Harry. Suddenly he burst into the kitchen and sat on the bench opposite me, squeezing in alongside Walter and Eddie. Daniel, Dinky and I were sitting on the bench nearest the window. Mammy as always was at the head of the table with Molly at the opposite end where Maggie, my other sister, would normally sit. Molly had already cut a whole loaf of bread into thick slices, each smeared with a thin layer of our precious butter ration.

Eventually, Mammy began to fill the plates. First came the bacon – a slice each for her, Molly, Daniel and Harry with a small portion cut off each for me, none for Dinky, Walter or Eddie. The cockles were ladled on next before finally we all had a dollop of laverbread, all that is except Dinky. The traditional Welsh way of serving laverbread

13

besides cooking it in bacon fat is to add vinegar and pepper. Mammy did this first for Walter and Eddie before the rest of us eagerly dived in.

It was then that Harry started his teasing. He was bolting his food down, but between swallows he began tormenting Dinky. "Go on mun Dinky 'ave some cow dung. It's lovely cow dung this is." Luckily for Harry, Molly was sitting near him and not Maggie. She was no match for him, but our eldest sister would have given him a clout without Mammy having to intervene.

"Stop that Harry," Mammy warned. "Leave the boy alone or I'll take your dinner away." Her words stopped his tongue for a moment, but he rapidly continued devouring his dinner, heeding her threat that he could soon lose it. Within a couple of minutes his plate was clean even though the rest of us had only just started to eat. This was his opportunity to create even greater mischief.

Where Harry was sitting, just out of Mammy's reach and close to the door, he knew that he could make a quick getaway. And he was going to need it. Molly wasn't going to stop him, so everything was in his favour for his next move. Casually he picked up a slice of bread held it in the palm of his left hand and then, without warning, struck like a cobra. His right hand shot out and scooped up Dinky's cockles almost clearing his plate. He was making a sandwich with them as he

bolted through the door and as if trying to justify his rotten deed shouted back to Dinky "If you can't eat the laverbread boy then you can't eat the cockles."

In a flash Mammy was blazing after him. "Iesu Annwyl. Wait 'till you get back. You'll get a good lamping my boy."

We were all left in a state of shock. Harry had spoilt the special Saturday dinner that we'd all been looking forward to. I felt angry, ashamed and sorry for poor Dinky who was now quietly sobbing. This in turn had set off Walter and Eddie. Hot and tired after sweating over the open fire cooking the dinner, Mammy tried to calm the little ones.

"Shh!!! Bachgen bach – hush little boys – come on, eat up before the food goes cold." Her soothing words did eventually stem the flow of tears, but an air of gloom had descended upon us. Harry had ruined everything. Thankfully, Molly, loving and generous as always, found the ideal way to cheer us all up. Ironically she had probably taken her inspiration from Harry and the sandwich he made as he ran off with Dinky's cockles.

"Look at me, boys. Look what I'm going to have," she giggled, picking up a slice of bread, waiting for a moment and keeping us all in suspense before revealing her intention.

"I'm going to make a Tarzan sandwich," she proclaimed.

As she did so Dinky's sad demeanour changed instantly to sheer delight – Tarzan was his hero. Molly plastered the bread with laverbread then added little bits of bacon before topping it with a heap of cockles and completing the sandwich with another slice of bread.

"Who's going to be first for a Tarzan sandwich?" she invited as she proudly held up her magical culinary creation for her eager young audience to scrutinise.

Dinky forgot all about his legendary dislike of laverbread.

"Me! Me! Me!" he shouted, determined to be the first boy to have a Tarzan sandwich.

His little face positively beamed as Molly handed it to him. Then, taking a gigantic bite he devoured it with relish. Of course Walter and Eddie now wanted Tarzan sandwiches too. They agreed with Dinky that it was the only way to eat cockles and laverbread. Molly had saved the day and everyone was happy again, but I don't think she realised just what she had started with her Tarzan sandwiches.

After dinner we went outside again, in search of any development

15

with the car that was now parked on the waste ground opposite our house. There was no sign of the owner or the older boys so we decided to give it a closer inspection. It was a black Standard 10 and must have once been quite a classy looking car in its prime before the rust and grime had taken hold. It now looked even worse as it sagged to one side with the loss of the front wheel. The bonnet was loose as well and half open and I realised why the car had bounced when it hit the bottom of the rough path – there was no weight to keep it down.

"Hey Dinky this car's no good mun. The engine's missing," I shouted. Dinky was making himself as tall as he could, stretching his small frame trying to look inside the vehicle, but failing. "Andy, gimme a lift mun. I can't see inside," he shouted back. He got his lift alright, but not from me. Two huge hands grasped him around his waist, lifted him way above the windows of the car and plonked him on the roof. For once in his life Dinky was speechless and so was I, for standing there was the man who had been steering the car earlier. I thought we'd be for it now, but fortunately for us he didn't seem to mind us looking around his car at all. The huge grin on his face reassured us of that.

"Well, what do you think of my car boys? Like it?" he inquired.

I had to answer truthfully.

"It's all rusty mister, the tyres are flat and the engine's missing." Then Dinky, who had recovered quickly from the initial shock of being lifted onto the roof of the car, chipped in.

"There's no seats mun and the wheel's come off," he chirped.

The man was still grinning as he lifted Dinky off the roof of the car and gently placed him on the ground beside me.

"Oh, we'll get all that fixed boys and you can help me," he said. "You can start today. Keep an eye on it for me, right."

Tom and his car, which would become a fixture opposite our house for the next four years, had arrived.

CHAPTER 2

Four boys and a wheelbarrow

The arrival of the long school summer holidays brought with it a host of fresh opportunities. I was ten and a half now, growing up and exploring the wider world away from the Hafod, the park and the Great Tip.

With lessons firmly at the back of our minds our little gang of friends wasted no time in getting down to business. On the very first day of the holidays we decided to set off on a hunt for jam jars in a bid to make some money. Jack Kramsky the scrap metal and rag and bone merchants were paying a penny for a pound jar and a halfpenny for a half-pound jar. This was to be one of Brammer Davies's better ideas, unlike his previous one at the balloon shed when the balloons turned out to be used condoms!

We always met at the lamppost on the square after dinner which could be any time between one and two o'clock. We rarely met in the morning, particularly if we were planning a long hike. We always ensured that we had our dinner inside and full bellies before setting off. And for me, there were always errands to run for Mammy. This was my primary contribution to the running of the Swain household. Mammy trusted me and I did my best not to let her down.

There was never any monetary reward for my efforts, but I did gain a reputation for reliability among our neighbours and very often I could combine running errands for them with those for Mammy.

When I did I would often be rewarded with the odd penny or two, a slice of home made cake or biscuits.

On this particular day, Dinky and Brammer were waiting there for me, eager to get started. Brammer was sporting a worn out, green Cub Scout cap and had an old wooden wheelbarrow in tow. It was almost as big as him and twice the size of Dinky.

"Hiya Andy!" he shouted.

"Look what Brammer's got to put the jam jars in."

As the gang's leader I was expected to give it the once over and my seal of approval. It looked a little battered and very heavy. I wondered how on earth he had managed to wheel it up the hill from the main road on his own. I soon found out when Dinky piped up.

"Tommy 'elped him to pull it up the 'ill mun – then 'e 'ad to go back 'ome for 'is dinner." He was referring to Tommy Thomas, the fourth member of our group. We were certainly going to need the big, strong and jovial Tommy with us if we were going to lug this thing around I thought as I gave it a nod of approval.

"Aye, it looks alright mun, but we'll 'ave to wait for Tommy before we start shifting it," I said.

But the boys were impatient. "We don't need Tommy by 'ere mun Andy," replied Brammer.

"It's all down 'ill to the main road. We can put Dinky in it and give him a ride."

On hearing this Dinky's eyes lit up. He thought this was a great idea and quickly clambered into the barrow, kneeling down with his hands gripping the sides. With an impish grin on his face he looked like a little bird sitting on a nest and was soon barking out orders.

"Come on mun, Andy. Grab an 'andle. You too, Brammer," he commanded.

We couldn't ignore him when he was in this infectious mood of mirth and mischief. We just had to go along with his wishes. So with Brammer on one side and me the other grabbing a handle in both hands we lifted the wheelbarrow and set off.

Aided by the slope of the road we soon gathered speed. We were laughing, whooping and screaming – until the wheelbarrow took over. At that moment we completely lost control. Brammer went down first, then me. As its wooden legs scraped along the rough surface of the road it came to a sudden halt catapulting Dinky into the air.

Fortunately, he landed on a patch of grass at the side of the road. I scraped my knee, Brammer cut his finger and lost his cap, but Dinky who should at least have been winded was up on his feet first.

"That was great mun. Let's do it again," he cried with glee.

For the moment I was too preoccupied with nursing my damaged knee. As I spat on the palm of my hand and rubbed the saliva into the broken skin, Brammer sucked noisily on his cut finger. To us youngsters spit could cure anything and was to be applied liberally to any wound. It was the immediate and universal antiseptic remedy for the misfortunes that came with our rough and tumble way of life.

The wheelbarrow however could not be mended so easily. The impact against the surface of the road broke one of its wooden legs and left the other in a dodgy condition. Brammer, who we now discovered had borrowed it from his neighbour without permission was looking decidedly gloomy.

"Oh Andy mun, Mr Lewis will go cowin' mad when he sees it," He said in a near whisper.

Before I could say or do anything we were distracted from our inspection of the damaged wheelbarrow by a figure racing down the road towards us. I recognised the heavy steps that were accompanied by a high pitched "Hiya boys!" immediately. It was Tommy Thomas. As he came closer he spotted the despondent look on our faces as we clustered around the wheelbarrow and guessed that all was not well. All too soon he realised the reason for our despondency.

"Oh 'eck Brammer, that's Mr Lewis's wheelbarrow. He uses 'at to get the dung off the road when the 'orses pullin' the ashcart 'ave a crap mun – puts it on 'is ruebob."

Until then it hadn't registered with us – particularly Dinky – that he had been wallowing about in a wheelbarrow that was mainly used for collecting horse manure. That wouldn't have mattered as it was Saturday, our regular weekly bath night and Dinky was smelling a bit ripe anyway.

I realised of course that Brammer shouldn't have taken the wheelbarrow without permission, but part of the trouble was its poor condition. Like Tom's car and many other things in our make do and mend world – like the country itself – worn out. One example of this was the bizarre, but not uncommon, spectacle of people riding bicycles without tyres. Boneshakers we called them. This was only

possible because, like the bikes themselves, the wheels were sturdy and made of steel.

Silence reigned as we stood there contemplating the sorry state of the wheelbarrow trying to work out what we should do next. I knew that looking at the barrow wouldn't mend it and some action on my part was needed.

"Right Brammer, I ordered. "Chuck the leg into the barrow. We can't leave it 'ere. Someone will 'ave it for firewood. Tommy, you grab the wheelbarrow and let's get going."

They all agreed and chorused. "Yeah. Let's get going mun."

For the moment at least we had found the solution. Like all typical nine and ten year old boys we decided to put things off and not face the music until we had to. I clearly remember thinking perhaps we'd find another wheelbarrow and then everything would be alright.

We had already lost the best part of an hour mucking about, but eventually made it down to the main road. Our little band turned right past Berry's the barber's, along past the post office and pubs and headed for Brynhyfryd.

Tommy was between the handles of the wheelbarrow resembling a horse between the shafts of a cart. He was a strong lad and could manage it easily on his own on the flat and going down hill. However, he did need our help going uphill.

We were heading into the unknown really. We were searching for the municipal rubbish dump where we believed there was an unlimited supply of jam jars. This information came from a very good source – my brother Harry. Wild, undisciplined, unruly, spiteful and selfish are just some of the words that come to mind when I think of Harry. But despite this he was streetwise. He'd been around and his information was generally sound although he did tend to exaggerate.

"Dinky and you collecting jam jars? I know where there's loads of 'em mun – up the dump, but you'll never find it," were his words when he had learned of our plans. This was typical of Harry. He loved to brag and swagger, giving snippets of information before drawing you into his web and making you beg for more. The fool that I was, I generally fell for it.

"Oh, Where is it 'arry mun?" I pleaded.

"Up the dump mun. It's too far for you," he answered with a mocking laugh. Still I persisted.

"Aw come on mun 'arry – tell us where it is."

Another clue followed.

"Don't be stupid mun," he answered. "It's past the newt pond and you'll never find it."

Well I knew where the newt pond was – past Brynhyfryd square near the road leading down to St Peter's Church. We had discovered it the previous year when Daniel, Harry and me were looking for blackberries. I had never seen anything like newts before. Frogs and tadpoles were abundant in the canal – and sticklebacks, but these newts seemed to be the only occupants of this silent little pond. They gave the place an air of mystery. To me it was part of an unknown world so I was glad I had my trusty little gang with me. We stuck together and had come through some hair-raising scrapes together.

We were on our way now. Under the railway bridge, past Pop's cafe and up a slight gradient to Silva's fish and chip shop. The road forked here and we went left, up Eaton Road avoiding two short, but steep hills, on the main Llangyfelach Road. Tommy seemed to be coping well with the wheelbarrow and there was no complaint from him, but Dinky was already starting to moan. He was tired and thirsty and wanted to ride in the barrow.

"Wait 'till we get to the newt pond Dinky, mun. You've never seen anything like 'em." My words were meant to offer encouragement.

Dinky had a vivid imagination and loved to be told stories. His eyes sparkled again as he said excitedly: "Tell me again Andy – what are they like? Are they slimy like frogs or frogspawn?" He was off now repeating all the daft things I had told him to wind him up and soon forgot how tired and thirsty he was. We were still in familiar territory. Just off Eaton Road was the Manor cinema, top of the list for the spending of any money we got for our, as yet elusive, jam jars. Sometimes, if we were lucky enough to have the necessary money, we would head for the Manor and thrill to the delights of Westerns with Roy Rogers or Gene Autry; or funnies with the Three Stooges and Laurel and Hardy.

We soon arrived at Brynhyfryd Square. It was quite a busy place, with shops and offices and people milling about – mostly women carrying baskets or shopping bags. Apart from the tradesmen such as bakers, grocers and deliverymen there would be few other men about. They would be at work in the factories and mills or down at the docks. I knew that by now it was after two o'clock as all the shops and offices were open again after having closed for dinner between one and two. We had to be extremely careful here as there was a lot of traffic – cars, lorries buses and horses and carts. It was a busy crossroads.

We tried staying on the pavement whenever we could, dodging between the shoppers and tradesmen which wasn't easy for Tommy and the wheelbarrow. There was some cursing and shouting going on about 'bloody kids' and soon Tommy was forced on to the road which was now on a downward slope. He was running at quite a pace towards the crossroads. I wasn't sure whether Tommy was pulling the wheelbarrow or it was pushing him. We all chased after him managing to dodge the odd vehicle here and there. Luckily, apart from some shouting and blasting of horns we got through the danger unscathed. With the rest of us in pursuit Tommy kept on running until we were all well clear of the square and its shoppers. Eventually the barrow came to rest on waste ground near some corrugated iron sheds.

The newt pond wasn't far away. It was more of a waterhole than a pond and soon the four of us were staring down at its murky waters, our eyes searching for the little creatures. The bottom of the pond was covered with a rust-coloured silt and there were bubbles rising from this indicating that there was a small spring underneath. Dinky was wound up now, but still there was no sign of the newts.

"Where are they 'en Andy? There's nothing 'ere mun," he said becoming increasingly impatient.

"Ush Dinky be quiet mun – you'll scare 'em off," I said, scolding him. Thankfully we didn't have to wait too long before a newt slithered out of the long grass that surrounded the pond. The four of us watched in fascination as it emerged. Brave Dinky was now clutching my arm and half hiding behind my back. Then a second one appeared and Brammer, with hand already in the water, tried to grab one. Dinky let out a squeal and Brammer missed it as the startled newts vanished.

Tommy reprimanded Brammer.

"Why'd you do that mun? I liked 'em."

"They're only tiddlers mun and Dinky's scared of 'em. But they don't frighten me. I could catch one if I wanted," came the reply.

But Dinky had had enough of newts.

"Come on Andy, let's go and find the dump," he said, pulling at my arm. I agreed and shouted at Brammer, annoyed that he had spoiled our fun and ridiculed Dinky.

"Come on let's go, you frightened 'em off. And why are you wearing that stupid cap? You look like a big sissy."

I knew my words would hurt him. That was the idea.

"My granny made me wear it see!" he retorted before adding "To keep the sun off my 'ead."

The cap brought back painful memories for me as a couple of years earlier I had tried to join the Cubs, but had been rejected because I couldn't afford the complete uniform. I resented him for both the moment and the cap. We went back to the sheds where we had left the barrow and continued on our journey. Tommy led the way pulling it, with me and Dinky close behind.

"I don't like newts Andy and I'm dying for a drink mun," he whispered to me, making sure that the others couldn't hear.

Brammer, suitably chastised, was a couple of yards behind dragging his feet with his head down. He was a plucky lad, but very sensitive. He was the only male in a house that seemed filled with women. We never went inside his house, always staying by the front door. Sometimes we could see and hear the women inside. They all made a fuss of Brammer, forever kissing and cuddling him, but I never found out which of them was his mother. The only one whose identity we were sure about was his granny, a plump, rosy-cheeked matron who was always in fits of laughter.

I knew his sulking wouldn't last long.

"Don't be stupid Brammer. Come up by 'ere mun," I called to him. He didn't wait to be told twice and was soon at my side, his arm around my shoulder with a mischievous grin on his face. There was no pavement on the road where we were now and it soon widened at a junction with three separate roads leading off a small roundabout. Tommy was still ploughing his way ahead.

"Oy, Tommy – go for the church," I shouted.

Without hesitating he kept going in a straight line over the roundabout before parking the wheelbarrow outside the gates of the church. We followed, but I went to the side of the building instead of the front. I had a surprise in store for them.

The church had a low perimeter wall of red bricks topped with iron railings, but tucked around to the left was the remains of an old stone wall with a small, rusty iron pipe sticking out of it. There was a constant trickle of water flowing from this pipe which my brother Daniel had shown me on a previous occasion. The clear, pure water was the sweetest I had ever tasted. I knelt down, cupped my hands and took a long, welcoming drink.

Tommy and the others came to investigate where I had got to and the three of them stood there with looks of disgust and amazement on their faces.

"You'll die mun, Andy," he exclaimed seemingly summing up the thoughts of them all. The three of them just kept staring at me, lost for words. I think they really did expect me to drop dead there and then.

"It's a spring mun," I said laughing.

"People 'ave been drinking from it since olden times."

I knelt down again and took another long drink of the water. This time, to emphasise just how good it was, I smacked my lips when I had finished.

"Mmm. It's great mun – the best water in the world. It's you who'll die if you don't drink it," I said, remembering what Dinky had said to me earlier.

"Right Dinky boy, you said you were dying for a drink, well drink now – or die," I told him.

He could see that I was not dead yet so it was a challenge he couldn't resist. Copying me, he knelt down and cupped one hand to catch the water, raised it to his mouth, then sipped it slowly. When he realised that he was not dying and just how sweet the water tasted he was soon cupping both hands and supping it loudly.

All thoughts of dying were now forgotten as Brammer removed his cap, pushed Dinky out of the way and not bothering to use his hands, put his head down under the pipe and let the water trickle into his gaping mouth. Not to be outdone I did the same and so did Dinky, the three of us relishing the refreshing taste of the cold, clear and sweet water.

That only left Tommy. He still seemed reluctant to drink it, but after some jibes of 'baby' and 'cowardy custard' from the rest of us he soon joined in.

Rested, well-watered and refreshed, we now had to decide which of the three roads in front of us would take us to the dump. This was as far as I had gone before. We were heading into uncharted territory.

I could see that the road to the right led down to St Paul's Church, where my family had taken refuge on the night we were bombed during the war, so it was a choice between the other two. I chose the middle road as it was a little wider than the one on the left. I was also intrigued by the steady throbbing and pounding noise coming from that direction and wanted to know what was causing it. Nodding my head in that direction and with Tommy leading the way between the handles of the wheelbarrow, we set off.

We were heading into a valley. The ground to the left rose sharply to about fifty feet before levelling off. On the right the river flowed down towards the church where it disappeared into an underground culvert that carried it under the road.

On the other side of the river the ground rose much higher, up to the remains of a building whose twin towers gave it the appearance of an old castle. This was a well-known landmark and could be seen from various parts of Swansea including the main road and the canal in the Hafod.

Harry had said that this building was haunted, but I didn't believe him. I'd had enough of Harry and his haunted houses, remembering the time when he got me to go into the Devil's Inn. This turned out to be occupied not by ghosts but by a man who was very much alive. As a result it was my intention to keep well away from the place and I fervently hoped that the dump we were so eagerly searching for was nowhere near it.

The banks of the river were quite steep and had already become heavily colonised by the ever-spreading Japanese Knotweed or as we called it 'German rhubarb'. This bamboo-like plant can grow to a height of ten feet and thrives on the poorest ground. It was flourishing along the railway lines, canal banks, industrial waste tips – almost anywhere it could establish itself. For imaginative ten year old boys it made a great substitute for the Amazon jungle or the Belgian Congo. Normally, without the wheelbarrow and our mission to collect jam jars, we would be fighting our way through it in the roles of Tarzan or the characters from the Lost World. But those adventures would have to wait for another day.

By now the road climbed slightly, but this didn't stop Tommy pulling the wheelbarrow for another hundred yards or so to where there was a bridge spanning the river. Just before that there was a solitary cottage, opposite which was a brick and mortar works. There were huge mounds of ash, stone and clinker some of which I expect came from the Great Tip that overshadowed our Hafod homes. The throbbing noise was coming from an old steam-driven generator. It seemed entirely out of place in what was otherwise such a tranquil, rural setting. There wasn't much activity, just one man with a pipe in his mouth who got up from the bench where he was sitting and took a few paces towards us. He had a hard look on his face. Without saying a word the man seemed to be letting us know that he was on his guard.

He was on to us.

Boys out of school, nothing to do, pushing a wheelbarrow – there's bound to be trouble and mischief there, he must have been thinking.

We didn't hang around and soon we were at the bridge that spanned the river. It was decision time again. Did we cross over or carry straight on? If we continued on our side of the river we would have to pass a long, ten foot high stone wall with a pair of large wrought iron gates.

The wall was lined on the inside with huge, broadleaved trees blotting out the sun from the road below. It was dark and gloomy there. In complete contrast, on the other side of the river the sun was shining. It would be warm and welcoming there. The only drawback was whichever way we turned we would be going uphill and would have to help Tommy with the wheelbarrow.

The decision was made as Brammer – without his cap now flung unceremoniously into the barrow – suddenly left my side and raced across the bridge.

"Come on mun, follow me," he shouted and with that he was gone, disappearing down the right hand side of the bridge. Something had obviously caught his attention and whatever it was he had decided he was going to be the first one there. The three of us raced over the bridge after him, to the point where he had disappeared. His sharp eyes had picked out a trickle of water flowing from an iron pipe embedded in the side of the bridge. He had found another spring and of course according to him the water from this spring had to taste better than the first one.

"It's a brammer mun boys – it's a brammer," he proclaimed to the whole world.

We all tried it and agreed. He was so proud of his discovery. Eventually we decided to continue in the same direction as before, but we had quite a steep slope to climb and even though Tommy did his best with the barrow he was soon puffing and blowing, eventually giving up on the task.

"You'll 'ave to 'elp me Andy," he panted.

"It's too steep by 'ere mun."

I was expecting this.

"Right Dinky, you get 'old of one 'andle and Brammer you get the other," I instructed.

"We gotta give Tommy a rest," I added.

Unfortunately this didn't work out, not even with a little further encouragement from me.

"Come on mun Brammer, you an' Dinky push," I pleaded.

They were no match for Tommy and couldn't budge it. Then they started to moan.

"It's not fair mun Andy you'll 'ave to 'elp us," they chorused.

Eventually, with me pushing and helped by Tommy for the latter stages, we got the wheelbarrow to the top of the hill. To our right was a short terrace of houses and on the left the ground sloped down to the river. Spanning this was a narrow wooden bridge, with a rough path leading up to the road on the other side. Directly in front of us, just after the houses, was the welcoming sight of iron railings with a pair of open gates painted in the mandatory council green.

It turned out to be a park and unlike Hafod Park which was small in comparison with its ash and clinker football pitch, this had acres of lush, green grass, trees of all shapes and sizes, some of which we had never seen before. To cap it all, the jewel in this municipal playground was a lake with a tree-covered island in its midst.

To our great delight we had discovered Llewellyn Park.

CHAPTER 3

The monster of Paradise Island

Our unexpected encounter with the paradise that was Llewellyn Park provided a rather startling distraction from our determined quest to discover jam jars. It was as if we had found our own Lost World. Hot and tired we pushed the wheelbarrow to the lakeside and sat on its grassy banks, silently scanning the lush, green and tree covered panorama.

"Did you know about this place Andy? It's great 'ere innit?" inquired Dinky.

I pretended I did and with an air of superiority answered "Yeah, mun." I wondered if Harry was aware of this place. I would be surprised if he wasn't. If he had discovered the elusive dump then he must have found this place.

Dinky just kept jabbering away.

"What do you think is over there Andy?"

He was pointing to the island in the lake which was about thirty to forty yards long and half as wide. His action was enough to spark off Brammer who was always up for a challenge. He was already untying his boots and soon these, and his socks, were off, quickly followed by his jersey, trousers and underpants.

"Come on Andy," he shouted. "Get in the nacker like me. Let's find out how deep it is." Soon the four of us were in the nude, wading tentatively into the cold water of the lake and making for the island with Tommy in the lead because of his height. Halfway across a nasty thought occurred to Dinky. With the water now lapping under his chin, he revealed his worst fear.

"Do you think there's newts in by 'ere Andy?"

He was out of his depth and frightened, but didn't want to say that and thought of the newts instead. The water was nearly up to Brammer's neck too, but he was determined to get to the island and was now furiously flapping at the water with his hands and feet. He was the only one of us who could swim or, to be exact, dog paddle and was soon pulling himself from the water up onto the banks of the island. Dinky however was stuck. He could no longer go forward as he was nearly out of his depth. The water level was around Tommy's waist and up to my shoulders. We could not lose face and go back so there was no option but to bounce Dinky up and down in the water. Tommy got hold of one of his arms and with me on the other we shuffled across to the island bouncing him up and down as we went. We shouted 'breathe in' on one bounce and 'breathe out' on the next, when his head was above the water.

By the time we had arrived at the island Brammer had already completed its exploration which must have taken him all of two minutes.

"There's nothing 'ere mun" he moaned. "Let's go back."

All I wanted to do was rest for a while as I collapsed to the ground and I am sure the others felt the same. Tommy seemed to be alright, but Dinky was coughing and spluttering; he must have breathed in when he should have breathed out.

"No, Andy mun. I'm not goin' back. I'm not goin' in the water again," he managed to utter as he struggled to regain his breath. For the moment I agreed with him – at least until I got my own breath back. Brammer meanwhile continued to moan.

"Come on mun, boys. It's no good by 'ere we gotta go an' get the jam jars."

To encourage us he jumped back into the water and he was soon, dog paddling back to the other side. We decided to ignore him knowing that he could be a bit of a show off. He could swim and we couldn't. The afternoon sun was scorching and the grassy bank on the island warm to our naked bodies. I lay back closed my eyes and took in the smell and feel of the new paradise we had discovered.

Unusually for him, Dinky too was quiet and Tommy never said much anyway, he was always happy to follow the lead. Even Brammer had stopped splashing about and was now probably getting dressed.

The luxury of silence and contemplation didn't last however. It was shattered by a high-pitched screaming and beating of the bushes in the centre of the island. We were frightened out of our skins which was apt given the naked state we were in. I sat bolt upright not daring to turn while Dinky screamed "Wassat? Wassat?" Tommy, with a huge splash, was in the lake. Dinky, who miraculously forgot his fear of the water, like me was not far behind. Although consumed with fear Tommy and I instinctively grabbed hold of Dinky and dragged him through the water back to the bank. The high pitched screeching and beating of the bushes continued until we were well out of the water. It had also scared the wits out of Brammer. We could see him jumping up and down running about, not knowing which way to turn until he saw us emerging from the lake. He was only half dressed.

"What's 'at noise?" he shouted.

Dripping wet and shaking with fright I could barely answer.

"I dunno. I dunno mun," I shouted back.

The four of us stood there looking across at the island, three naked boys and Brammer, with just his jersey and socks on. Our eyes scanned the trees and bushes in a bid to catch a glimpse of whatever was hiding there. We were transfixed, like statues waiting for some dreadful, horned creature to emerge and warn us to keep off its island.

Our voices dropped to whispers.

"Ooo, I'm scared mun Andy," wailed Dinky.

"Let's get dressed and go 'ome."

"Aye boys. Get dressed quick," I said, echoing his feelings.

Without taking our eyes off the island we put our clothes on in world record time. Dinky's mother would have been proud of him, particularly if he could get dressed as quickly as this every school day morning. Brammer kept moaning he couldn't find his cap.

"Never mind about yer cap Brammer mun," I whispered. "Get yer trousers on. Tommy, you grab the wheelbarrow and run for the gates. We'll keep watch by 'ere until you're in the clear."

It was downhill all the way to the gates and Tommy was off at a trot, while the rest of us backed away from the lake still scrutinising the island. We didn't see anything, but suddenly there was a short, sharp cry. Where it came from I didn't know, but it sparked us into full flight and fits of screaming as we streaked passed Tommy and reached the gates before him. We kept on running with Tommy shouting "Wait for me! Wait for me!" until we reached the path that led down to the river and the small wooden bridge. It was only then that we stopped and turned, hands on knees, panting for breath, to see if there was anyone – or anything – pursuing us.

By the time Tommy reached us he was out of breath and his legs were wobbling as he let the wheelbarrow go and collapsed in a heap on the floor. The wheelbarrow kept on going and ended up halfway down the rough path which was enough to send us all into uncontrollable fits of laughter. This certainly relieved the tension of our scary experience in the park.

Dinky was sure we had been attacked by an evil spirit.

"It was a ghost, mun. Only ghosts sound like 'at," he said.

But Brammer had the answer and chided him saying.

"You're daft mun, Dinky. It can't be a ghost. They only come out at night. It was an invisible monster mun – that's what it was."

Ghost or monster I was not sure what it was. I was just glad that we had got away from it safely – albeit with the loss of Brammer's cap.

Our next move had already been made for us by the barrow which was half way down the path to the river, so we continued down to the wooden bridge that spanned it. We managed to cross this, but with some difficulty. Tommy and me were pulling the barrow with Dinky and Brammer pushing from behind. Eventually we got it up to the other side of the valley. We emerged near the high stone wall that I had seen earlier. After the exertion of our flight of panic the shade of the trees alongside it was welcoming. I now had to decide just what our next move should be. If we turned to the left the road would take us back to the bridge and the mortar works, while to the right it disappeared around a bend in the direction of the park.

Dinky made his feelings known right away.

"I'm not going back in that park Andy boy. Not for you, not even for the King." Brammer agreed with him. "Not on your life, Andy boy," he said defiantly.

However there was a third option. The high wall which ran along side the road stopped here and turned sharply. Then, further up the road, there was a row of cottages with long narrow gardens. Between these and the wall was a rough gravel track, just wide enough we thought to take the council ash cart. Unusually for him Tommy now seized the initiative.

"I bet the dump is behind that wall, Andy," he said.

"Up that lane and behind the wall."

"It must be Andy," said Dinky keen to add his six penn'orth.

We've been everywhere else Mun – it must be up 'ere."

I agreed. It was the only option left open to us unless we turned back and headed for home.

"OK. But don't blame me if we end up in Timbuktu," I warned.

We were in light shade to start with, but the deeper we went into the lane the darker it became. The sunlight was unable to penetrate the dense foliage and so it was cold and damp. I felt a shiver as Tommy, who was leading with the wheelbarrow began to quicken his pace. As we hurried behind him Dinky began to get the jitters.

"I don't like this place Andy. I got goose bumps on my arms," he whispered. Quiet as his voice was Brammer still heard him and was not going to be outdone.

"I'm shivering too Andy," he said.

"I got goose bumps all over."

Thankfully their whingeing was cut short as Tommy suddenly came to a halt. There was a wooden five bar gate blocking the path. On it was a sign with the warning that proclaimed 'Keep out – Trespassers will be prosecuted.'

Fortunately for us a pair of large black iron gates similar to those we had seen earlier offered a passage through the high wall. They were open and had no threatening sign. Inside there was a narrow tarmac road flanked by bushes which disappeared round a sharp bend.

"See Andy, I told you," said Tommy, with authority.

"I told you this would be the dump, didn't I?"

Puffing out his chest with pride he picked up the barrow and strode through the gates.

The rest of us trooped behind, not knowing where we were going until we got around the bend in the road. I had no idea whether it was the dump or not, never having seen one before in my life. But that soon became immaterial for we were suddenly faced with another unexpected surprise on our day of discovery. What greeted us shocked and horrified me. It wasn't the dump at all – we were in a graveyard!

Tommy was deflated now. His earlier swagger, when he thought he had found the dump, was gone. He dropped the wheelbarrow to the ground and stared ahead, open mouthed. The rest of us clustered around him. This was the last thing we had expected. Graveyards were definitely out of bounds for children – especially boys with a barrow.

"So this is the dump, is it Tommy? " said Brammer, laughing.

"Looks more like a graveyard to me Tommy boy."

I had been to a cemetery before, having visited my own father's grave several times over the previous year. Accompanied by Mammy and the rest of the family I wasn't too bothered, but I certainly would not visit one out of choice. Tommy was still in a state of shock, but Brammer did not seem to care at all. He was still gloating at Tommy's embarrassment, Dinky was a different matter – he was terrified.

"I don't like this place either, Andy," he whispered, pressing ever closer to me.

"It gives me the shivers. Let's go back."

Revelling in Dinky's discomfort and Tommy's embarrassment Brammer had other ideas.

"No mun, I've never been in this graveyard before. Let's have a look around," he said.

He loved to show off and was full of himself as he raced away from us to the first row of graves. Most were marked either by a mixture of different sized headstones or simple wooden crosses, but to the left of the road was a cordoned off area with large marble tombstones. Brammer was peering down at one of the graves and starting to read aloud the inscription on the headstone.

"In . . . loving . . . memory . . . of . . ."

He didn't get any further as his words were suddenly interrupted by a high-pitched screech coming from the direction of the large headstones. We had been frightened when we had heard a similar noise in the park earlier, but now, in the graveyard we were absolutely petrified. The brave Brammer couldn't manage a scream, not even a pathetic yelp as he sprang away from the grave he was inspecting and raced back to us. Tommy dropped the wheelbarrow once again as me and Dinky, both shaking with fear, clung on to him. Brammer was soon hiding behind me and, like us, was quaking in his boots.

"It's the invisible monster from the park" he stuttered.

34

"What are we goin' to do, Andy?" said Dinky about to burst into tears at any moment.

We were almost level with the gravestones, but such was my fear I was afraid to expose my back. I did not want to return to the dark lane with this thing about – whatever it was. We crept forward with the only sound being the creaking of the wheelbarrow on the tarmac surface. But we didn't get more than a few paces when there was another ear-piercing scream that stopped us dead in our tracks once more. Instinctively we looked towards the source of the noise not knowing what would happen next.

Just when we were expecting to meet with certain death – or an even worse fate perhaps – a broom handle rose from the centre of the tombstones resting on top of which was Brammer's cap. This was the last thing we had expected. We stared in disbelief as the cap was waved from side to side by an unknown hand behind the tombstone. Even more intriguing came the sound of chuckling as a tall, skinny boy emerged holding the pole in both hands. About the same age as me, but taller, he was dressed in a white shirt and brown baggy trousers with highly polished brown shoes. He walked slowly, but confidently towards us with a broad grin on his small face, stopping about three feet away before lowering the pole and depositing the cap at our feet.

It was immediately obvious that this boy was not from a working class family, he was posh or as my mother would say – Crachach. His dark hair was short but not cut in a short back and sides like ours nor a napper head like Dinky. It was layered evenly all over with a parting in the middle. For a while everyone was silent. Then he spoke.

"I am Eric. Who are you and what are you doing with that wheelbarrow?" he said clearly, pronouncing every syllable.

Not one of us replied. We were confused I suppose. A moment before we had been scared stiff, expecting to be attacked by a monster, but now we were being confronted by a prissy young boy demanding to know why we had the wheelbarrow – and he was the one who had pinched Brammer's cap!

Awaiting a reply which wasn't forthcoming he cocked his head to one side and without taking his eyes off us slowly began to circle around us. Although I was still wary of this stranger my earlier fear was gone and I quickly regained confidence. He had completed the circle and was standing in front of us again, but his grin had vanished.

"Who do you think you are boy? The king like?" I said, mustering as firm a voice as I could and almost shouting out as I stared straight at him. With that he held his arms up in a gesture of surrender and his small mouth broadened into a grin. He stepped towards me and offered his hand.

"How do you do – my name is Eric. What is yours?"

I had seen men and women shaking hands, but never children and I didn't know what to do next. Mimicking him I just stuck my hand out which brought fits of laughter from the other three. Of course that set me off and soon we were all laughing including Eric who had slipped his hand into mine and given it three good shakes before releasing it. Then the taunts began from my pals. First it was Dinky.

"You do look daft, Andy, " he said.

Then it was Brammer's turn.

"You look a proper sissy mun, Andy."

"Shurrup mun Brammer, an' you too Dinky," I replied.

It hurt being called daft and a sissy, but then unexpectedly Eric came to my rescue – inadvertently maybe – when he said.

"Dinky and Brammer, what sweet names – and you are Andy."

Then suddenly Tommy, who had been left out of things, chipped in rather sternly with "An' my name's Tommy Thomas." It was as if he was indicating that he had a proper name and wasn't to be thought of as sweet like Dinky and Brammer. Our meeting and conversation with this strange boy had me confused. There was something odd about Eric and Brammer was the first to spot it.

"Hey! Wait a minute you're not a boy, you're a cowin' girl mun," he suddenly exclaimed stunning us into a temporary state of shock as the four of us closely scrutinised Eric. He didn't look like one of us but I thought that was down to him being a bit posh.

"Are you sure you're not a girl?" I asked.

"Well, I am a girl really. My name is Erica but I prefer to be called Eric," she replied completely unfazed.

So she was a girl, but dressed like a boy and was not in the least concerned what we thought of the fact.

"Why do you need a wheelbarrow? Are you gathering wood or something?" She asked returning to her original question.

"Nah, not wood mun, jam jars," muttered Dinky before I asked her if she knew where the elusive dump was.

"You mean the council dump?" she said.

"The rubbish dump mun – where the ash carts take the rubbish," I replied not really sure. Her reply brought bad news.

"Oh Dear!" she said solemnly. "That's a long way from here. It's beyond the park up near the old quarry."

"It's a dangerous place and it will be dark when you get there."

Her words seemed to change the whole atmosphere of this once exciting new world we had entered. The afternoon sun which was blazing earlier was now shaded by clouds which only added to our sense of gloom. Even Brammer had lost his interest in the gravestones.

"I don't like it by 'ere any more Andy," he muttered.

"Let's go 'ome."

Two minutes later, with the girl who thought she was a boy leading the way, we trudged out through the cemetery gates. Erica lived in one of the big houses that stood opposite and before she left us she issued an invitation.

"You must come again – to find the dump; and you must bring a bigger wheelbarrow as it is absolutely crammed full of jam jars," she said before turning and running up to the gates of the big house.

"Cheerio! Cheerio!" she shouted, "I'll look out for you when you come again."

Soon we were making our way past the mortar works. There was no sign of the man now but in his place was a big black dog which didn't budge as we passed. It just sat there and growled menacingly. Once we were clear of the place Dinky in a low, fearful voice muttered "That was a black wolf mun." Nobody argued with him. We were too tired and fed up for that. Then he ran off.

"I'm going to be first to get a drink," he shouted back at us after he had gone a little distance down the road towards the spring near St Peter's Church.

It is surprising just how quick a return journey can be at times and soon we were back in the Hafod, trudging up Pentremawr Road towards the square where we had all met earlier. However there was one more hurdle for us to overcome. Waiting there for us was the owner of the wheelbarrow – Mr Lewis. I had never met him, but Tommy, still pushing the wheelbarrow, recognised him straight away.

"Cowin' 'ell Brammer – it's Mr Lewis mun," he exclaimed.

We all stopped dead in our tracks – except for Brammer that is. He kept on walking straight towards the man.

"Look Mr Lewis, we found your wheelbarrow," he said to him without a care in the world.

"Over by the tip it was and someone's broke it too."

We didn't expect the old man to believe him. We thought he'd go berserk, but amazingly he took hold of Brammer's hand and walked him back to us. We hadn't moved and Tommy just stood there his mouth open, but still holding the wheelbarrow. Contrary to what I thought, Mr Lewis was not a bit annoyed at the state of it he just seemed relieved to have it back.

"Well it's not bad boys, is it? Only the legs have come off and we'll soon fix those won't we?" he said with a wink at Brammer. I could hardly believe my eyes. The cheeky rascal had got away with it. But that wasn't enough. "Give us a ride – Mr Lewis," he asked the old man as he took the wheelbarrow from Tommy. The old man just nodded and Brammer jumped in. With a big grin on his face he waved to us as he was wheeled away. As he ran after them Tommy shouted "So long boys – see you tomorrow." to me and Dinky.

It was Dinky who neatly summed up our expedition.

"Well we didn't get any jam jars after all, and that girl who thinks she's a boy is a strange sissy," he said

He was right. We had failed in our mission to find jam jars and his remarks about Erica were spot on.

She was indeed a strange girl.

CHAPTER 4

Finding the river
and a lost sister

There was just one solitary week of the summer holidays remaining and I was seriously looking forward to the routine and discipline that a return to school would bring. There was little adventure or excitement to fill my days and boredom was setting in. Part of the reason for this was that my best friend was missing. Dinky had gone on holiday to Weston-super-Mare to visit his paternal grandparents.

Life might have been busier had there been an invitation to help with the harvest on my uncle's farm. This year however, as if to make matters worse, none was forthcoming. There had been some changes in Mammy's family. My Uncle Idris had got married and moved to his new wife's farm. This meant unfortunately that he could no longer look after Mammy's youngest brother, the lovely, but childlike Uncle Jack. I never found out what happened to him except that he did not accompany Uncle Idris to his new home. Perhaps he was taken into care by another member of the family or to a home for the mentally handicapped. He may even have died. I just didn't know.

Mammy's estrangement from her family since she had gone to live 'in sin' with my father was still a sensitive issue and contact with them was almost non-existent. Her father's disowning of her was still very evident. She was not considered worthy enough to be invited to my Uncle Idris's wedding. In fact I don't believe that she had been in contact with him since the summer of 1942 when Daniel, Harry and myself stayed at the farm and had an encounter with Mario an Italian prisoner of war. Perhaps, sadly, she was thinking about her family and her early life on the farm when one day she decided to re-visit a place from her childhood days. This was on another farm, near the village of Llangyfelach, where Mammy had spent many happy days with an aunt and her family.

Mammy kept things close to her chest and when she did take us out for the day she seldom told us exactly where we were going. Instead she preferred to allow things to develop as the day unfolded. More often than not it was usually to visit my father's grave anyway. But on this particular day we set off in search for 'the river' – one that Mammy remembered from her childhood days at the farm. There were six of us in tow – Maggie, Daniel, Harry, Walter, Eddie and me. Maggie, who worked for the Star Supply Stores in Swansea, was with us so it must have been a Thursday, the quietest day of the week when the shops there closed for a half day. Mammy probably chose this particular day as she liked to have Maggie around to help keep control of us boys. My other sister Molly had finished her secretarial course at Gregg's College and was working for a firm of solicitors in Swansea. Like most office workers her half-day was a Saturday.

We caught the No. 77 bus which passed through Morriston on its way to Pontlasse, a hamlet on the road that runs over the hills to the Amman Valley. Near where we left the bus was a five-bar gate. Mammy guided us through this and along a track hemmed in by hedgerows. The weather was warm with a breeze and good for walking in the country. Mammy was carrying an old shopping bag which held our refreshments for the journey – a lemonade bottle filled with water and one of her famous rock cakes already cut into seven slices. She also had an old biscuit tin with a lid to hold any blackberries we might find. The bag was made from the tough material used for barrage balloons during the war. When they came down, either through enemy action or some other cause there was always a scramble by people living near where it landed to get their hands on the fabric.

As we ambled along the farm track we settled into our normal formation. Mammy and Maggie led the way holding the hands of the younger Walter and Eddie. Me and Daniel followed closely behind

40

with my errant brother Harry running ahead or lagging behind as the mood took him. It would be a miracle if five minutes ever elapsed without Mammy or Maggie having to rein him in with a series of warnings or threats to his life to behave.

Mammy always warned us to be on our guard whenever we visited the countryside. She said that though it might look serene and peaceful we should be prepared for the unexpected. She told us we should stick together to avoid getting lost and beware of farm animals and be especially aware of vipers – Britain's only poisonous snake. She had repeated her warning as the place we were about to visit she remembered from her childhood as being notorious for vipers. She said she'd heard of men dying after being bitten by them.

"Children would have no chance of surviving a bite from such a snake," she warned grimly. Now while the rest of us took this warning seriously Harry, as always, saw things differently.

"How far is the river now Mammy? I want to see the vipers," he repeated continually when he was ahead of us, but then he would dash back past me and Daniel, creep up behind us and so that Mammy couldn't hear him would taunt us in whispered tones.

"I'm going to get a viper to bite you 'andel."

He was always trying to frighten me so I just stayed close to Daniel. I knew that I was safe as long as I was with him.

After we'd been walking for about twenty minutes we came across another five-bar gate after which the track widened and finally, there in front of us, was the river. It was much wider than I'd expected and

the water level was quite high for the time of the year. Spanning it was an old, but sturdy, wooden bridge with a ford on one side which allowed animals and vehicles to cross.

"Here we are," said Mammy proudly. "This is the river."

She had special childhood memories of it which she wanted to share with us and she smiled with satisfaction at the scene. We all stood silently respecting her achievement in guiding us to a place she had last visited more than twenty five years before. Her pleasure and the silence was short lived as the bridge proved too much of a temptation for Harry who was racing across it and scampering up and down the bank on the other side. "Gan bwyll! Gan bwyll! – Careful! Careful!" Mammy shouted after him. She always reverted to her native tongue when angry or scolding one of us. For most of the time – as on this occasion – her anger was directed at Harry.

There was no handrail on the bridge, but it was wide enough not to cause any problems as long as we crossed in single file. Daniel went first with me following, then Maggie with Walter and finally Mammy and Eddie. She was extremely cross with Harry for misbehaving and he knew it as he kept well out of her reach for the next ten minutes or so. But that did not stop him from calling me.

"Come over by 'ere Handel mun come and see the fish," he said.

He was stretched out on the riverbank now, his head almost touching the water. Then he was up again shouting, still trying to get me to join him.

"There's no vipers – 'onest mun."

To ignore or refuse him was courting disaster so I pretended not to hear him, but Maggie came to my rescue anyway.

"Don't you dare, Handel boy. You stay by us," she threatened.

"We don't want to go chasing after two of you."

There were some blackberry bushes nearby and we spent the next half an hour gathering what we could. They were mostly green or red as it was still too early in the season really, but we did get some which were ripe. When we had finished we sat on the grass near the bridge for a moment. Mammy took the bottle of water from her bag.

"Have a little sip to keep you going," she encouraged the three of us youngsters. We drank eagerly from the bottle but she, Maggie and Daniel didn't seem as thirsty. She didn't bother with Harry. She knew that when he wanted one he would demand a drink. Mammy was ready to move again. She called Harry who was now throwing stones into the river to join us.

"Come on Harry and stop doing that," she scolded.

"There'll be no cake for you my boy."

There were far more trees on this side of the river and the farm track that we were now on passed through a dense wood. Every so often Mammy would stop and inspect various trees.

"What are you looking for Mammy?" asked an intrigued Maggie.

"Nuts, Mag," she replied.

"If I remember right there are some good nut trees around here."

Her memory didn't fail her. She was soon tugging on the branches of a tree, then holding out the palm of her hand to reveal maybe a dozen slender hazel nuts, but they were still very green and hard.

"They're not really ripe mind Maggie but we'll take them. They might be ready in time for Christmas," Mammy said to Maggie as she put them into her bag.

Harry's curiosity got the better of him and he joined us as we clustered around Mammy to see the nuts. He hadn't helped in collecting the berries, but nuts – they were different. He liked nuts.

"Come on 'andel come with me mun," he said as he sidled up to me. "There's loads of nuts in these woods. We won't wait 'till Christmas mun. We'll eat 'em now."

Once again I was rescued from his clutches; this time by Mammy.

"No! No! Boys bach – you stay close to me and we'll find plenty of nuts along the way," she said.

I did as I was told and stayed close to her, but not Harry. He was off up the track, running from side to side and darting from one tree to another in his search for nuts. He was soon back into the woods. The rest of us were content to follow Mammy as she carefully studied the trees and picked the odd few hazelnuts here and there.

We could hear Harry thrashing about in the woods. Sometimes he would reappear on the track and then disappear off the other side. He hadn't found any nuts or he would have been back boasting and showing them off to us. Mammy was not worried about this. As long as she could see or hear him she was happy. It was when he was out of sight and quiet that it was likely he was up to no good.

We had probably been walking for about half an hour since leaving the river when we came across a small clearing where the farmer had stacked lengths of wood. Mammy decided that this would be a good spot for our picnic and we each had a piece of cake and a drink of water. Although it was only a mixture of lard, flour and water with sugar and currants mixed in, Mammy's rock cake was considered a luxury and one sure way of enticing Harry out of the woods. Two magic words soon had him scampering towards us.

"Harry – cake," shouted Mammy.

Harry was in a dreadful state. There were twigs and leaves caught up in his jersey, his boots were scuffed and his legs and trousers were covered in mud. This didn't unduly alarm Mammy. A bit of spit and the cloth she always carried with her would soon get most of the mud off. Harry was aware that he was going to get a clout around the back of the neck but he wanted his cake so he had no option but to endure the punishment. Mammy knew that it would not have much effect anyway, but at least it gave vent to some of her frustration with her wayward son. What he had not bargained for and what he did not know about until Mammy had got hold of him by the scruff of his neck was that he had torn the seat of his trousers.

Clothes were expensive and hard to come by, especially outer garments like jackets and trousers. These were his school trousers and soon to be handed down to me. Mammy realised some extensive repair work would be needed if they were to be saved. She could contain her anger no longer an almost exploded, raining blows on Harry's back and shoulders as out came the Welsh:

"Iesu Annwyl of Nazareth. What am I going to do with you boy?"

Mammy's grip was like a vice, but today for the first time ever that I could recall Harry managed to wriggle free. He grabbed a piece of rock cake that she had set out for us and shot off up the track back towards the river. Maggie gave chase for a minute or so but she had no chance of catching him and soon gave up. Mammy however was quick to regain her composure, resigned to the fact that Harry would always cause problems.

"Oh, let him go Mag. He'll soon find us – no doubt."

After we had rested, eaten our cake and drunk some water, we were on our way again and soon emerged from the woodland area. Once again the farm track cut through green fields flanked on either side by hedgerows. On one side was a large meadow where the land rose gradually for about a quarter of a mile then dramatically altered rising sharply. I could hear the faint, but distinct trill of a skylark as it climbed into the sky above us. In contrast to the green fields below it, the hill looked threatening with its darker brown hue. I would have expected to see sheep grazing there but it looked barren – a cold and lonely place.

Mammy had promised us nothing when we embarked on this journey, but there'd been a hint that we might possibly see or visit her aunt's farm which she had sometimes been to as a child. Sure enough, after we had been walking for a little while, there stood the farmhouse. Built of stone with a heavy grey-slated roof it was a square, rather lofty building with the usual cattle sheds, stables and barns around it.

"Is this where your auntie lives, Mammy?" asked Maggie.

We did not have many aunts and uncles that we were in regular contact with and were excited at the prospect of meeting a new relative, albeit a great aunt. We began to bombard Mammy with a string of questions.

Our excitement started my two younger brothers Walter and Eddie shouting and jumping up on the five bar gate at the farm entrance. This in turn roused a dog that came bounding out from the farmhouse barking furiously and scaring the wits out of us all, especially Walter and Eddie who abandoned the gate and ran to the safety of Mammy.

"Hush now – all of you" she said.

"You've gone and woken everybody up."

Then to pacify the dog she spoke to it in Welsh.

"Dere, dere ci bach – Come, come little dog."

Immediately the dog stopped barking and trotted towards us wagging its tail in recognition of a friendly voice.

Mammy was only too aware of the monotonous routine that most small farmers endured. Early to bed and early to rise. Day in and day out, the cattle had to be milked twice a day, with no let up. So it would be normal for the occupants of the farmhouse to be taking their customary nap after dinner, a well-earned rest before the second milking of the day. That precious nap had just been rudely brought to an end by the noise and commotion of our arrival.

Fortunately it was the farmer's wife, a placid lady as it turned out, who emerged from the farmhouse slightly dishevelled and rubbing her eyes. She was a sturdy, grey haired woman, clad in a Fair Isle jumper, a black skirt and wellies.

"Shw'mae, shwd y chi?" Mammy said in Welsh. The words meant hello, how are you?

The woman returned her greeting and they started a conversation in Welsh, none of which to my frustration, I could understand. It all seemed friendly enough but very formal, not what you would really expect between two long-lost relatives. There were a couple of Duw, Duws expressing surprise and Mammy looked perturbed at one point.

I knew when the conversation had come to an end as Mammy uttered the words "Diolch, diolch yn fawr."

I knew this meant thank you, thank you very much.

Once more we were on our way as the farmer's wife waved goodbye. We all felt a bit dejected as Maggie asked "Mammy, why didn't your auntie ask us in?"

"Wait! Hush girl," she replied, with a note of caution in her voice.

I noticed a slight change in her manner. She had quickened her pace, no longer ambling along the farm track. I was also beginning to suspect that there was a lot more to this trip than visiting the river and looking for nuts and blackberries. She continued hurrying along, waiting until we were well out of sight of the farmhouse before she slowed down and answered Maggie's question.

"That wasn't my Auntie Jane, Maggie. She's dead. That good woman just told me now. Died last year, she did."

She paused wistfully, but didn't seem saddened by the news, just slightly puzzled.

"Nobody told me, mun," she said.

And then, as if she could not believe it she repeated the words.

"Nobody told me."

Quickening her pace again she strode on, arms swinging and lengthening her stride. She had that stern look that hinted she was on a mission.

Maggie was taller than Mammy now and could more than keep up with her, but was aware that the rest of us, especially Walter and Eddie who were being dragged along by me and Daniel, were struggling.

"For goodness sake Mammy, slow down!" she exclaimed.

"If your auntie's dead, why are we rushing like this?" Maggie was the only person who could speak to Mammy in this way. They were almost equals now. She had taken on the burden of helping to raise the family and keep it together since the dark days of 1941 when my

46

father was killed and we were bombed out of our home. Mammy took heed of Maggie and her pace slowed. I think her turn of speed was because she was annoyed at the news of her auntie's death. It was just another reminder of her alienation from her family. Harry must have been on her mind too, as there had been no sign of him since he had run off earlier.

When Mammy finally found herself able to answer Maggie's question her words brought with them a shock. They rocked Maggie.

"It wasn't my Auntie Jane that I wanted to see mun. I was looking for her daughter Megan," she said.

She paused for a moment. Then, after taking a deep breath, delivered a staggering revelation.

"You see Maggie, Megan was not her daughter really. She was my mother's daughter – my sister."

For once Maggie was dumbstruck. I was bewildered and so was Daniel, as Mammy continued her tale.

"She couldn't have any children see Mag, and my mother already had three – me and two boys from my father's first wife, so she gave Megan to Auntie Jane."

Mammy realised that this news had come as a bombshell to Maggie and quickly added "It was the thing to do in those days. Families were very close."

She hesitated again before continuing.

"Mind you I don't even know if they bothered to tell her. They just wouldn't think about it. To them it was the natural thing to do, then."

We continued walking at a more leisurely pace – in silence now – as we tried to come to terms with the strange story of Mammy's sister Megan. She took hold of Eddie's hand once more with Maggie holding on to Walter. Mammy eventually broke the silence to encourage us and keep our spirits up.

"It won't be long now boys bach. We'll soon be coming to Llangyfelach. There's a shop there, maybe we'll get some pop and catch the bus there. Is it? " she said. Then the question of Harry's whereabouts was revived.

"What about our Harry, Mammy? Don't you think we ought to go back?" asked Maggie.

"Too far to go back now Mag. Don't worry about Harry, he's thirteen now and I expect he'll be home before us."

It wasn't long before we came to the end of the farm track with its five bar gate. This opened onto a narrow road which led down to the main road. In the distance we could just see the steeple of Llangyfelach church. The day was still warm although dark clouds were building, threatening rain. Mammy sensed this as she hurried us along repeating her promise.

"Not long now and we'll get some lemonade, right."

She had tremendous stamina, whereas the rest of us, including Maggie, were glad when we eventually reached the village.

Mammy we discovered was on a quest to find her sister who she had been told at the farm lived in Llangyfelach. Like any village the local shopkeeper knew all of the residents and probably most of their business too. So it was no surprise when, after buying the promised pop, Mammy emerged from the shop with an address.

We were near the village green with a public house on the other side. There was also a bus stop and Mammy pointed to a wooden bench near this, gave two small bottles of lemonade to my sister and issued her instructions.

"Nawr te, Maggie, the shopkeeper says the bus will be along in about half an hour, so take the boys and wait over by there for me. I won't be long."

Maggie wasn't happy with this. She was curious to see what Mammy's sister looked like – the mysterious sister that we had never heard of before.

"Well can't I come with you Mammy," she protested.

"Daniel can look after the boys. They're no trouble without Harry."

Surprisingly she agreed and the two of them hurried off along the main road with Mammy studying the house numbers as she went. She was right. They hadn't gone far when they stopped and Mammy knocked on the door of one of the houses. She had to knock hard a second time before eventually a man opened the door. Soon he was joined by a woman who, even from a distance, I could see bore a striking resemblance to Mammy. It looked like she had at last discovered her long-lost sister.

The man disappeared back inside the house leaving the woman on the doorstep deep in conversation with Mammy. I thought it odd that Mammy had not been invited into the house. The two of them stood there talking for about ten minutes then with Maggie walking behind them, the woman accompanied Mammy back to the village green where we were sitting. Maggie sat next to Daniel on the bench. She was not a happy girl and shouted at Walter and Eddie.

"Stop that noise you two," she said scowling.

They were a bit noisy and running about on the grass, but not doing any real harm or making a nuisance of themselves. But they did as they were told and sat quietly now. They knew better than to upset their big sister.

Mammy and her sister Megan stood slightly apart from us continuing chatting and I could fully understand now why Maggie was upset. They were talking in their native Welsh and of course she couldn't understand a word they were saying. Although she was seventeen and had matured fast, as far as Mammy and her sister were concerned she was still a child. Because of that she had been excluded from the conversation.

The whole meeting between Mammy and her sister seemed strained and uneasy. They were strangers and had nothing in common. Her sister was perhaps influenced by their extended family while Mammy had been excluded. Megan was married now, but childless and one would have thought that she would gladly welcome Mammy – with her seven children – back into her life. Sadly it was not to be. The reunion was polite but not warm. They were both probably glad when the bus finally arrived and they parted without even a handshake. It was possible that her sister even resented Mammy because she remained with her parents and Megan had been given up. Perhaps even Mammy did not know the entire truth for seeing the two of them standing there side by side they were like peas in a pod. I have a feeling that they were in fact identical twins.

Unfortunately, when we eventually returned home and the prospect of normality, the wishful thoughts in my mind that my brother Harry had got himself lost and I would never see him again proved to be wrong. He was sitting on the wall outside the house knowing and expecting that he was going to get a hiding from Mammy.

As usual he tried to delay his punishment for as long as possible, got off the wall and ran across the road to the tip when he saw us approaching. Surprisingly Mammy who was probably feeling tired and dejected just called to him. "Dere, Harry bach. Come on boy. Come in now and have your tea."

So ended our first trip to the river and the place where Mammy spent many happy days of her childhood.

She didn't let the disappointment of her sad reunion with her sister deter her from going back there and several times during the following few years we not only returned to the spot, but went even further and explored the mountain we had seen in the distance on our first trip. It was an incredible place, the whole mountain appeared to be covered by molehills. On sun-filled summer days we would climb to the top and picnic there with a bottle of pop and some Welsh cakes, watching and listening to the skylarks.

The day after our first memorable trip to the river Mammy made blackberry tart – tart in more ways than one since sugar was still very scarce. The nuts we stored in the attic kept until Christmas, but we had picked them too soon and they weren't ripe. When we eventually retrieved them during the festive season we were disappointed to find that they were mouldy and rotten.

CHAPTER 5

In the money and hot water

The last week of August was always a testing time for Mammy. It was a time of mixing and matching, repairing and darning, all in preparation for our return to school after the long summer holidays. There were only the four of us still in school now – Harry, Walter, Eddie and me. Maggie, Molly and Daniel were all working and contributing to the family purse. Even so there was little money to spare and we still had to make do and mend.

Despite this Mammy put money aside each week to buy more and better household items. Our latest acquisition, as a result of her thriftiness, was a battery-powered wireless on hire from Dan Morgan's electrical shop in High Street. The battery was about half the size of that on a car and had to be taken back to the shop weekly – every Tuesday in our case – and exchanged for a replacement while it was charged ready for collection the next week. It was a delight to be able to listen to the wireless again – and in my own home.

There is no doubt that its arrival helped relieve the tedium of the final few days of the holidays at least until the Saturday when my best pal Dinky returned from his holidays in Weston-super-Mare.

Dinky had an infectious personality with a stoked-up imagination and I knew that he would be full of outrageous tales about his exploits while he was away. With his inquisitive nature he would also want a full account of what had been happening in my family during his absence. He loved being at our house with all its comings and goings and the racket generated by seven children. I think he spent more time with us than he did at his own house. Although wary of Harry, he was happy to play with Walter and Eddie if for some reason I wasn't around. His mother used to tell Mammy that there was one thing for sure – if he was not under her feet she always knew where to find him.

Dinky and I had already made plans for what we were going to do when we grew up. Working on the docks or in the copper works was not for us. He was forever nagging me to tell him stories of our future plans. I had visions of a more adventurous and romantic life for the pair of us based mainly on the exciting tales of Robin Hood and his Merry Men.

Naturally, as the leader of our gang, I would be Robin Hood. As for Dinky, although highly unlikely because of his small stature, he opted to be the giant – Little John. He had managed to convince me that like the fictional character he too would grow and develop physically into a man of huge proportions. This was defying all the odds as, like him, both his mother and father were rather small people. Still he believed that it was possible and anyway what he lacked in bodily size and strength he made up for with his noisy and boisterous character. Brammer Davies and Tommy Thomas were also included – as Will Scarlet and Friar Tuck.

Should our Sherwood Forest fantasy ever become reality I had Daisy Davies marked down as my Maid Marian, though she was never aware of this. Dinky insisted on having his Maid Marian too, a girl by the name of Biddy Roberts who occasionally came and stayed with her granny next door-but-one to him. We would scorn the use of modern weapons such as guns and instead rely solely on a long bow and quiver of arrows. Although living off the land and feasting on venison, unlike our hero we didn't fancy the idea of living in the forest. We were going to commandeer one of the many Norman castles built in Wales for our stronghold.

I often thought that this make-believe world provided an escape for Dinky from the increasingly difficult circumstances of his family life now his abusive father had returned from the war. The change in his personality was not obvious, but he was slowly becoming less confident and losing his impish sparkle and wit. Perhaps that was one of the reasons why Dinky spent so much of his time in our house despite the noise and commotion often evident within its walls.

When we did eventually return to school and face the old routine again, I was in standard three, Mr Richards' class, or Baldy as he was known to his pupils, a nickname earned for obvious reasons. He was a short, dapper man with sharp eyes, always alert and constantly on the move. He was a very talkative character with a loud voice. On the whole Baldy was well-liked by his pupils, but there were occasions, if a boy was silly enough to incur his wrath, when punishment would be swift and painful.

Baldy Richards had an uncanny ability of hand to eye co-ordination and could bring down a fly at a distance of twenty feet using the stick of chalk he always carried in his right hand as a missile. This could be dispatched without warning and would unerringly find its target, usually the bridge of the nose or between the eyes of any errant boy deemed to be guilty of talking or not paying attention. Older children would warn those about to enter standard three of Baldy's unique Dead Eye Dick ability with a stick of chalk and the necessity of not taking their eyes off him for a moment. Consequently he probably had the most attentive class in the school, if not the whole world and youngsters of a nervous disposition, always expecting the worst, would instinctively duck if Baldy made any unexpected moves.

This was to be my only term with Baldy Richards, for at the start of the New Year I was moving up to standard four. We had been told there were many changes in the nation's education system over the next year or so which would come in three major stages. The first of these was the abolition of the old scholarship examination where the children lucky enough to pass attended grammar school. Under this system certain children would be given more than one chance to pass. This was to be replaced by the 11-plus, a once and for all exam with no second chances. Also, the school leaving age was to be increased from 14 to 15 and the start of the school year was to be switched from January to September which meant that I would be gaining some new classmates and losing others.

Harry was in his final year at school, but unlike the rest of his classmates who were now all wearing long trousers, he was still in shorts. Bafflingly, there was a pair of hand-me-downs from Daniel that he could have worn which would have signified one more step on the path to eventual manhood, but he preferred to stay in his shorts. Perhaps for all his bravado and contempt for others he was fearful of growing up even though it seemed to me that he still had the same selfish and abrasive attitude to life, bullying all and sundry whenever he thought he could get away with it.

It was at this time that our church-going days, of three services every Sunday and singing in the choir, came to an abrupt end. The choir was supervised by Mr Bowen the organist, a heavily built, middle-aged man who was extremely strict. He seemed well suited to be in charge of a choir that consisted of half a dozen men and a dozen or so boys.

Surprisingly, given the two personalities involved, during the entire time that Harry was a chorister I cannot remember a single occasion when he fell foul of this man. So it came as a shock when one Sunday morning as we were assembling to leave the vestry, just before the start of the service, Harry in a fit of rage, removed his surplice and cassock, threw them to the floor and ran out of the back door of the church.

It was bang on eleven o'clock as the vicar entered the vestry and Mr Bowen hastily departed to take his place at the organ. Then Daniel coolly removed his surplice and cassock and told me to do the same. That signalled the end of the Swain brothers as choirboys. On this occasion Daniel had backed Harry. He believed his brother had done no wrong and together we showed our defiance to the world as brothers united.

Why Harry reacted as he did remains a mystery, but apparently Mr Bowen had said something to him which had obviously touched a raw nerve. For a while we continued to attend church, sitting in the third row behind Miss Whitehorn and the little ones which now included Walter and Eddie. It was never the same after our walk-out though.

The autumn of 1946 marked the passing of two years since Harry and I had stolen a railway lamp. The punishment ordered by the Juvenile Court was a severe warning for me and two years probation for Harry. It was his second offence and he was warned that if he appeared before them again he would be sent to an approved school or borstal. Everyone agreed that we had got off lightly, but we had both learned a valuable lesson and Harry had come through weekly sessions with a probation officer with flying colours. So fortune did not smile kindly upon the Swain family the day Harry struck up a friendship with another odd character – Islwyn Smith or Issy as he was known.

Issy was a sly character, lanky and smelly, with dark curly hair. To look at him you would think that he had nothing in common with Harry, but as I was to discover he did – a compelling desire to take, by fair means or foul, whatever he could lay his hands on.

No one realised that since they had teamed up these two seemed to have new found wealth as they embarked on a lifestyle totally out of keeping with two lads from relatively poor households. Visits to the Manor cinema in Manselton which changed its films twice a week were on their agenda as well as trips to the cinemas in town which normally we could only dream of.

This wasn't all however. They also seemed to have no problem getting their hands on sweets, ice cream and fruit which were becoming more plentiful in the shops now. They were even smoking the best Players cigarettes rather than the Woodbines they would usually have bought when they could scrape a few pennies together.

Things came to a head when they went into Swansea late one Saturday afternoon and caught the train to Mumbles. After having a good time at the resort things turned sour when they either missed the last train back or ran out of funds to pay the return fare. Anyway it was very late that Saturday night when Harry arrived home to one of his customary hidings from Mammy.

Next morning Issy's mother turned up. She was an enormous, harsh-looking woman who wore what looked like a man's double breasted raincoat and a large black beret that covered part of her streaky blonde hair. She had painted nails, rouged-up cheeks and thick red lips. This fearsome looking woman demanded to speak to Mammy – urgently and in private.

It was nearly time for Sunday dinner, a weekly event that was considered special and a time when we all sat down to eat together. Everything was on the go – the meat in the oven and the vegetables in their pots clustered around the open fire.

This didn't matter.

Both women disappeared into the front room as the rest of us huddled together in the kitchen with Maggie and Molly, their ears pressed to the door, trying to listen to the conversation which got rather heated at times. Eventually Mammy opened the door and returned to the kitchen. I could see that she was in a distressed state, marching furiously into the room, her eyes blazing.

"Iesu Annwyl Harry!" she screamed.

"Where are you? You'll end up in jail, you devil."

Of course there was no sign of Harry. He was long gone. Anticipating why Mrs Smith had descended upon us he had quietly slipped away as soon as the two women had closed the door of the front room. We all remained silent. We hated it when Mammy was in this angry mood.

"Right. Maggie – and you Daniel," she ranted.

"Go and find him at once. He's in big trouble now."

There were more instructions as the rest of us continued to wonder exactly what misdemeanour it was that he was guilty of.

"And don't come back without him," she called after them.

We all knew that there was little chance of Maggie and Daniel finding Harry, but whatever had transpired between Mammy and Mrs Smith had deeply upset her and she wanted to confront Harry in this woman's presence before deciding what to do. He would hold out for as long as he could to avoid facing the problem. This would usually

be until his stomach was crying out for food. Only then would he come home. Sure enough, after a few minutes Maggie and Daniel returned without him. By running away Harry had added to Mammy's dilemma and she now returned to the front room to speak with Mrs Smith once more. Eventually Mrs Smith left, but not without first issuing a warning to Mammy that was so stern it sent a shudder through us all.

"If I don't get the money Mrs Swain – the whole five pounds, three shillings and sixpence – it will be the police for you and borstal for your son," she said as she went through the door.

When Mrs Smith had gone Mammy sat down, her head bowed. She was exhausted with the worry and stress of what had just occurred. We were all a little shocked by the sudden intrusion into our life by this big, brassy and loud woman who for some reason felt she was in a position to threaten our family. Maggie was incensed by this and could hold her tongue no longer.

"What's wrong, Mammy? What's Harry been up to again? Who is this woman coming here and threatening us?" she demanded. Mammy said Mrs Smith was a collector for a loan company that issued cheques which could be exchanged for goods at various shops. The loan was then repaid with interest over a fixed term and payments collected by agents such as Mrs Smith.

It all came out that Saturday night when Issy had returned from the jaunt to Mumbles. Mrs Smith, anxious to learn how he could afford such a trip, put him under considerable pressure until he confessed to helping himself to the money.

The scheming Issy had put all of the blame on Harry claiming that he had put him up to it. Mrs Smith would have been in a weak position to back him up if she hadn't discovered that Harry had recently been on probation.

Armed with this knowledge and believing that Harry was totally to blame she was threatening to report the matter to the police if Mammy didn't pay up. The outcome would have been a further court appearance by Harry and an almost certain custodial sentence.

Whether Mrs Smith would have carried out her threat was another matter, but Mammy couldn't risk this and during the following weeks she handed over the sum of five pounds, three shillings and sixpence. It was an extremely large sum of money and it took our family many weeks to recover. Christmas was looming and any spare cash that Mammy might have for buying presents was gone.

Harry was eventually given a good hiding by Mammy, but she had come to his rescue once again. If he had gone to borstal, away from the family influence, I have no doubt that a life of crime would have followed soon after.

Amazingly, although Harry seemed to prove to everyone that he was hard to almost anything life could throw at him, he seemed visibly shaken by this event and for a while his attitude softened, but this didn't last long. He soon regained his arrogance and was back to being the brash, selfish individual that we all knew and recognised.

CHAPTER 6

Cold days and warm thoughts

Christmas was always a special time – even without presents – and that of 1946 was no exception. I was nearly 11, and I still hung up my stocking on Christmas Eve as did my two younger brothers, Walter and Eddie. The basic stocking fillers that we excitedly woke to on Christmas morning were always the same – an apple, an orange, walnuts, hazel nuts and some Brazils or horseshoe nuts as we called them. If we were lucky, now that the sweet ration had been increased there might also be half a bar of chocolate and a few Mintoes.

Despite the huge dent made in Mammy's savings by having to repay Issy's mother she had somehow managed to gather a miraculous festive spread and top of the list was the chicken for Christmas dinner. Mammy never failed to find a chicken after the disaster of 1942 when we had to make do with a rabbit.

This year there was even a home made Christmas cake that had been baked in the local baker's oven as well as my favourite – a rich, fruit-laden Christmas pudding.

According to the comic books we all eagerly poured over at that time all our favourite characters like Desperate Dan or Pansy Potter hungrily tucked into plum duff, a plain suet and flour pudding with a few currants and raisins in it. I painfully remember Maggie cuffing the back of my neck for referring to Mammy's Christmas pudding as plum duff. Her words carried a particular tone, were straight and as usual right to the point.

"Listen boy," she remonstrated.

"Mammy makes proper Christmas pudding with loads of fruit and candied peel – and a bottle of Mackeson stout. So don't you dare call it plum duff again."

Apart from that minor setback it was a pretty good Christmas. It turned out that we had some presents after all. Mammy and my two sisters had managed to scrape together some extra cash and as a result I got a small pencil torch. This meant I could now read at night without having a candle stuck on the top of the bedstead. That was good fun while it lasted, but unfortunately by New Year's Day the battery had run out and there were no funds available for a replacement. The luckiest boy in our house that year though was my eldest brother, Daniel.

Like Molly, Daniel had completed his book-keeping course at Gregg's College and was starting work with a firm of chartered surveyors and auctioneers immediately the festive season was over. His present this year, an essential one, was a new pair of black shoes. There would be no more hobnail boots for him.

Daniel's office was only minutes away from the solicitor's where Molly worked and they caught the No. 73 bus into Swansea together every day ready to start at nine o'clock. As a shop girl, Maggie on the other hand, had to be in work by eight o'clock.

It was a good thing that we did have a happy Christmas for with the coming of the New Year the Swain family was in for its worst time since the early days of the war and Swansea's Three Nights' Blitz.

With the arrival of the New Year I was moving up to standard four in school, something I had serious reservations about. They were based partly on the schoolyard tales of older boys, particularly Harry, and about my new teacher, Beaky Jones, someone obviously nicknamed because of his resemblance to a certain species of bird.

Beaky Jones had a reputation for intolerance of disrespectful and inattentive boys that made him the most feared teacher in the whole school. He was even scarier than the head teacher, mighty Joe Morgan. Beaky was of medium height with fair, thinning hair, watery blue eyes and a pale complexion. In fact an appearance very ordinary apart from one outstanding feature – his magnificent bird-like nose. Coupled with the tales of doom related by older boys it conjured up a vision that he would turn into a terrifying bird of prey and rip out your entrails should you incur his wrath. The frightening thing was that the point of this transformation was unknown which was enough to make most boys – even our Harry – wary of him.

As it happened my classroom life with Beaky had to wait as another devastating force was about to grip the country in a life-threatening stranglehold – the weather.

The winter of 1947 was one of the worst on record. It was as if a mini ice age had descended on us. For the first few months after the Christmas holidays we could not really get settled into our new classes. Learning became something of a stop-start affair because of the bitter cold, snow and ice. Schools would open and close depending on the severity of the weather. Children would still be expected to attend school every day at nine o'clock only to be sent home if the head teacher thought it wise to close.

Conditions were horrible for everything except for one thing, making slides. Even if the school closed for the day the playground remained open and the older boys would make ice slides across it. All they required was a heavy frost and if it was covered with an inch or two of snow so much the better. They created the first two or three feet of the slide by rubbing the soles of their boots or shoes on the ground until a patch of ice was formed about eighteen inches wide. Once the first patch was slippery enough they would each line up, take a short run up and with one foot in front of the other and arms outstretched would slide forward. Each time someone did this the length of the slide would increase by a few inches. Within a short time it would stretch for almost the entire length of the sloping playground, fanning out to the right and left at the bottom as each boy finished, curving away from the perimeter wall at the bottom end.

Needless to say some of the more inexperienced or those who were just plain reckless ended up smashing into the wall, often with some fairly dire consequences.

Because hobnail boots were not allowed on the slide me and Dinky never got a look in, but I will never forget Brammer's first go. We stood and watched as he joined the line of older boys and, whooping and screaming, took his turn on the slide. Disastrously, he lost control halfway down and over he went, with his forehead making contact with the ground first. Fortunately for him a good coating of snow that day helped cushion the blow, but he still ended up with a lump on his head the size of an egg. We took him straight home and his granny put some vinegar and brown paper around the lump. By the following day he was raring to go again — back on the slide.

Apart from the bad weather there was also a transport strike in the London area and a severe coal shortage. Bread was becoming scarce and for the first time potatoes were rationed. Despite this Mammy once again made sure that our bellies were always full. Probably the biggest threat to our survival that cold winter was the lack of coal. Supplies were sporadic and sometimes we had to make do with coal eggs – coal dust mixed with a binding agent and moulded into egg-shaped lumps. It was dreadful stuff which gave off an incredible, dense smoke and burned to a very fine, powdery ash. Still it was better than nothing.

It was during this time of coal shortage that we once again turned to that wonderful benefactor that helped us survive the war – the huge mountain of waste from the furnaces of the old copper works – The Great Tip. Its height had been considerably reduced by the Yanks during the war, notably Sergeant Nick and his bulldozer. Thankfully his work had exposed new seams of half-spent coal and cinders which were regularly exploited by families struggling just like ours.

During this particular winter however there were many more people scouring the tip with buckets, scraping and scratching away for reusable cinders. Even families who were quite well off and would ordinarily never need to resort to such behaviour could be seen foraging on the tip.

Mercifully, after what seemed like an age, the Arctic conditions began to release their icy grip by the middle of March and life slowly returned to normality.

CHAPTER 7

Interrogation at the kitchen table

E arly one Saturday evening in the spring of 1947, the whole family gathered in the kitchen to witness an auspicious event. As usual Mammy sat at the table, her back to the fire with Maggie alongside her. On this occasion both faced a young man who was being put under close scrutiny by Mammy.

Sam was the first and only boyfriend that Maggie had brought home. They had been courting for just six months and this was his third or fourth visit. The reason for it soon became obvious – Sam was asking Mammy for Maggie's hand in marriage. He was 19, just a year older than Maggie and within weeks he would be on his way to join the Royal Navy to do his National Service.

Sam's current mission however would involve a battle of wills. Not between him and Mammy though. Instead this tussle was between Mammy and Maggie as it was she who wanted this engagement and she usually got her way. Mammy was asking questions with narrowed eyes and her jaw set firm. Sam would have been no match for her on his own, but on this occasion, with Maggie there to put steel into his back, he stood an even chance of getting the right answer.

"Well Sam, do you think it is wise getting engaged before you go off to the Navy?" began Mammy. "Eighteen months is a long time. Are you quite sure that you will feel the same way after you've done your National Service?" Mammy had fired the first barrage of questions in her interrogation, but it wasn't likely to be the last.

Sam, an only child, was quite a tall young man with dark wavy hair and brown eyes. He was sitting with his back almost against the bathroom door with his legs crossed and hands clasped firmly in his lap. As he answered Mammy, in a soft, quiet voice his eyes were fixed firmly on Maggie.

"I'm quite sure Mrs Swain, I want Maggie to be my wife more than anything else," came his answer.

He hesitated for a moment as his eyes darted from Maggie to Mammy and then back again. I could sense that my sister was willing him to be more positive. Sam who had just finished his apprenticeship at a ship repair yard down at the docks was struggling to find the right words, but a glare from Maggie prompted him to break the silence.

"I wouldn't do anything to hurt Maggie, Mrs Swain, and I've got a good job waiting for me when I return from the Navy," he blurted out in a single breath.

There was a lull in the interrogation after Sam had said his piece. Mammy was waiting to hear more. If he intended to take away the main help and breadwinner from the family then he was going to have

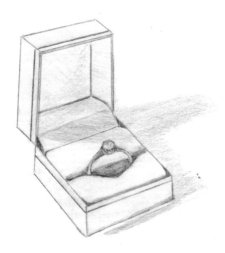

to work harder for the privilege. With my brothers I silently witnessed the whole tense scene as it unfolded. The five of us were lined up against the kitchen window, facing directly across the room towards the table where the main protagonists were battling it out. My other sister Molly was standing behind Maggie, no doubt under instruction from her older sister to provide moral support should Mammy turn awkward. No doubt too she was picking up valuable pointers for when her turn came in the marriage stakes.

I could see Maggie's fixed and stern expression with her fierce eyes drilling into Sam's skull as she willed him to continue with a dialogue they had probably already rehearsed countless times. Spurred on by this, if perhaps a little hesitant, he eventually continued.

"Oh yes, Mrs Swain, my mother said to tell you that when we get married we can live at our house," he said.

Another brief pause followed before Sam spoke again.

"Until that is we've saved up enough for a deposit on our own house," he said. This was intended to be his trump card.

Maggie probably thought that getting Sam to show Mammy that he intended to become a house owner, would do the trick, but what followed was not what she or Sam expected.

"Oh, so your mother knows about this, does she?" exclaimed Mammy indignantly as, eyes blazing, she turned to Maggie.

"I see. So you've discussed this with his mother is it, before thinking of telling me."

She was angry now and right on cue out spilled the Welsh.

"Diolch yn fawr, merched. Thank you very much, my girl."

Maggie's reaction was just as typical. She wouldn't be intimidated by Mammy and her response was just as fierce.

"No, Mammy, I have not discussed this with Sam's mother or anybody else for that matter. Sam only told her what he intended doing and that's all."

She hesitated to ensure her words and her timing were right in an attempt to inject a little guilt into Mammy's heart.

"So there Mammy, Sam's mother is helpful and very pleased about it. She wants me to marry him," she added defiantly.

Mammy's reply was devastating. It was not at all what Maggie or

Sam wanted to hear or had planned for. She stood up and wagging her finger at Sam began to berate his absent mother.

"Do you think that his mother is at all concerned with you?

"She's not worried about you girl. All she knows is that her little boy is leaving home. She wants to tie him down so that he'll return when his service is over."

In another life I'm sure that Mammy would have made a fine lawyer. Her brain was razor sharp and her tongue like a rapier when she felt she needed to protect her own interests along with those of her family. Having to survive alone for so long had produced a streak of cynicism in her. She could be highly suspicious of people's motives.

"She doesn't want him running off with a girl from Portsmouth, Plymouth or even Hong Kong," she continued.

"So don't think that she's got your best interest at heart my girl. I'm telling you, she hasn't."

I looked at Sam. He was downcast. The last thing he or Maggie wanted now was an argument between these two feisty women. Fortunately for him and the rest of us Molly came to the rescue. She was there to support to Maggie, whose blood we could all sense was coming to the boil, and that is exactly what she did.

"Give Mammy a look at the ring Sam. Show her the engagement ring mun."

Molly had taken the sting out of things. She had stopped Maggie from exploding and answering Mammy back which she knew would only have made matters worse. Maggie was still furious, her round eyes bulging, but wisely she took her cue from Molly and kept her mouth shut.

Sam fumbled in his coat pocket before producing a paper bag. From this he clumsily extracted a small square box. Molly knew that she was pushing her luck with Mammy but she chided Sam for fumbling with the box.

"Come on mun Sam, hurry up! Mammy wants to see the ring. Don't you Mammy?"

Eventually Sam's shaking fingers managed to open the box before thrusting it forward in Mammy's direction.

At that point we just couldn't resist the temptation to see for ourselves what all the fuss was about. All five of us boys with Harry leading the way pushed forward to the table. The sight of this engagement ring brought a chorus of ooos and aahs from all of us, except that is Mammy who was still eyeing Sam with more than a hint of suspicion.

Maggie, whose look of fury had now been replaced with one of angelic radiance, simply couldn't wait to get her hands on it. She took the box from Sam, removed the ring and slipped it onto the third finger of her left hand. Then, with an almost regal presence, she stood up and held her hand out in front of her, proudly displaying this bejewelled token of love for all the family to see.

"Look Mammy," she cooed, her voice soft and tender, "Solid gold it is, with three real diamonds and all set in platinum."

Seeing the ring on Maggie's finger seemed to do the trick as Mammy's previous reluctance to accept the engagement softened.

"It's a lovely ring Mag," she conceded.

Then with a deep sigh she launched her final salvo.

"But it takes more than a gold ring with three diamonds to make a happy marriage my girl."

With these words and from her change of attitude it looked like Mammy was about to give her blessing to the engagement, but from past experience Maggie knew that her mother was not finished yet. Mrs Bennett, Sam's mother, had so far appeared to have set the agenda for the forthcoming engagement to tie him down to returning home after his service, as Mammy had pointed out.

Now she had some tying down of her own to do.

"This has all got to be done properly mind," she insisted, the authority back in her voice after a brief submissive lull.

"It's got to be announced in the Post mind," she said, referring to the South Wales Evening Post, the paper such local news had to appear in to be considered official.

"For all to see and know. I don't want any promises made and then broken," she proclaimed as if to stress the point.

I didn't realise the significance of these words at the time, but Sam and Maggie knew only too well what she was getting at. Mammy wanted the engagement broadcast to the world. She would only give her consent when she had concrete evidence of Sam's intention. She had to see the announcement in print. Then, so there was no misunderstanding, she pointed at the ring on Maggie's finger.

"So until I see it in the paper my girl, you can take that off and put it back in the box," she said.

Maggie realised that there was no point in arguing any further as Mammy had more or less agreed in principle to the engagement. She quickly replaced the ring in the box and grabbed Sam's arm.

"Come on," she ordered, as she marched him through the door.

"We're going to see your mother now. I want this in the Evening Post on Monday."

CHAPTER 8

The trials of Big
Chief Broken Knee

The day after Easter Monday 1947, marked the beginning of the Easter holidays from school for me and I was happy at the prospect of a long lie-in. My brother Harry on the other hand would enjoy no such luxury. For him the day marked a new beginning. Mammy had secured him a job in the local copper works and he had to get up at six o'clock so that he would be ready to start work exactly one hour later.

Harry was no longer a schoolboy. He was grown-up now and for the first time in his life was wearing long trousers. He was following in the footsteps of our father, grandfather and even great-grandfather. Our father had worked there continuously, apart from his war service, for 33 years until he was killed in a bombing raid during 1941. Harry was 14 and one of the last youngsters to start work at this age as the school-leaving age was increased to 15 soon after. In future he would have to work for five and a half days a week with Saturday afternoons and Sundays off. Holidays would be restricted to two weeks in the summer – always the last week of July and the first week in August – and bank holidays.

Harry's job was to assist the cook in the works canteen and, as with most boys leaving school with no qualifications, he would start at the very bottom. In his case this would mean scrubbing floors, washing dishes and general fetching and carrying. The one great benefit of this particular job, and something which may have played a part in Mammy's decision to put him forward for it, was that he was entitled to free meals. Harry was a lump of a boy now, not very tall but broad-shouldered, stocky with stout limbs. His arms resembled tree-trunks and he was immensely strong. He had a voracious appetite and would steal the food off your plate if he could, so the knowledge that he would be fed at work must have been a great relief to Mammy.

It was hard physical work but that suited Harry. No one could accuse him of being afraid of hard work. The saying that 'the devil finds work for idle hands' could have been written with Harry in mind. He was a much better person when his mind and hands were fully occupied. Having said this I suspect there were moments of idleness when mischief beckoned and he allowed his tongue to take control of his brain. Reports began to find their way back to Mammy of Harry being cheeky and insolent at work. Apparently he'd been giving some lip to the men. It was only the intervention of some of my father's former workmates that saved him from a good hiding.

At about this time the big freeze of 1947 finally released us from its icy grip and life began to return to normal in the school yard after the holidays. The main winter game of football was played enthusiastically while the usual spring and summer games slowly began to assume their usual seasonal popularity. There was Hide and Seek, or Mob as we called it for the smaller children. Games like hopscotch, skipping and rounders were firm favourites for the girls while for the boys it was Dandies, Cat and Dog, Marker and Weak Horses.

Dandies was sometimes known as Jacks or Fivestones and involved tossing five shiny pebbles into the air before attempting to catch one on the back of the hand and letting the others fall to the ground. The pebble would be flicked up again as you scooped up one of the others from the ground before catching it again. This would be repeated until all the pebbles had been picked up. Then the game would start all over again, but with the added requirement that two pebbles had to be scooped up. So it progressed until all four pebbles were being picked up at the same time.

The whole sequence needed to be completed without any drops. If one did occur then you would have to start all over again. Most boys would be happy to complete the first stage but the more skilful would progress to elaborate and difficult variations like clapping hands or spinning around while the pebble was in the air. This sometimes resulted in painful consequences for the player if he misjudged his timing as the pebble dropped back down.

Cat and dog was another game which required good hand to eye skills and yet again could produce some painful consequences. Not for the player this time, but anyone unfortunate enough to be caught in the line of fire. The game was played with two sticks – the dog which was the longer stick and anything between one and two feet long and the cat which would be about six to nine inches long and tapered to a point at both ends.

The object of the game was to hit the cat with the dog. To achieve this the cat was placed on the ground where it would be struck on one of its tapered ends with a mighty downward blow. This would send it twisting and flying into the air. This was when the player had to prove his skill in timing and judgement. As the cat, still spinning, fell back to earth he had to strike it in mid-air and how successful he was would be judged by the distance the dog had hit the cat.

Of course the science of the operation left a lot to be desired as generally both sticks were rough and crudely made and there was no guarantee that the cat, once struck by the dog, would fly off in its intended direction. So anyone within a radius of ten or twenty yards would be in an extremely perilous position indeed. Needless to say the game was banned from school playgrounds.

Marker and Weak Horses are derivations of Leap Frog or as we called it High-Backs. This was usually played by the younger children and modified to suit older boys. This kind of game was never played in the girls' school. It would usually start with a couple of the younger boys discovering and playing High-Backs and would quickly spread throughout the school until some of the older boys got involved. They would transform the proceedings into the more complicated game of Marker. This involved laying down a mark, a line scraped on the ground, with the heel of a boot or shoe. Then the first boy or marker, would stand on the line with his hands on his knees and create a back. A procession of five or six boys would then attempt to vault over him.

Anyone not performing the vault cleanly with even the slightest of contacts against the boy bending would be the next marker. If more than one lad made a mess of it then there would be two markers. The game was restarted by one of the boys – usually the biggest – taking one stride from the mark and the marker would then create a back there. Similar strides were measured out if there were two or more. Of course this made the game more difficult. The players now had to take a run up to the mark before springing from it and vaulting over the boy or boys bending. This could number as many as six or seven in a really good game.

Very little harm came from playing Marker as physical contact was only one on one, but Weak Horses was an entirely different matter. In this there was serious risk of harm to life and limb. The number of boys participating was much greater and could involve up to twenty or more depending on how it developed.

Once again the game was started with a volunteer – known as the horse – making a back but this time facing a wall with his hands placed firmly against it. Then, one at a time the rest of the players would take a running leap and straddle his back. Generally by the time that the third boy landed on him he gave way and collapsed. He was considered a weak horse and was replaced by those boys who had brought him down. So with three boys making backs now an even greater number of players would be attracted, all taking flying leaps and straddling them until breaking point was reached, resulting – in further weak horses. Of course all those going down, as many as eight or nine boys would then form the next line which in turn would attract more players as the shout went up – 'long horse, long horse!' – bringing boys running from all corners of the yard.

The scene that subsequently followed was a sight to behold as boy after boy, caught up in the excitement, went flying onto the line until finally the legs of the horses buckled under their weight, bringing down into one gigantic heap twenty or so screaming, yelling and writhing bodies. Some boys would emerge from this scene of chaos relatively unscathed, but others came out of it battered and bruised. Unbelievably after a brief rest they would be up and ready to start the game all over again.

Dinky and I continued to live in our imaginary world of Tarzan, Robin Hood, and Cowboys and Indians and it was during one particular episode when we were in our imaginary Wild West that I sustained one of the worst injuries of my young life. I was pretending to be Geronimo the Red Indian chief and Dinky was the kind of cowboy character that would have been played by actor Tom Mix. He was galloping off after firing his imaginary guns at me when I went to respond with my bow and arrow.

I knelt down in the classical stance and was pulling back on the string of the bow to put an arrow deep into his back when I felt a searing pain in my right knee that took my breath away. Gasping in pain I looked down only to discover that I had been maliciously attacked by the jagged bottom ring of a broken milk bottle.

I had sustained many cuts and bruises in my short life but I was shocked by the amount of blood gushing from my split knee. Dinky in the meantime was making his return gallop to deliver a further salvo from his six shooters only to be greeted with the gruesome sight of me clutching at my knee, yelling and screaming.

"Look at my knee mun Dinky," I screamed at him.

"Look, I'm cowin' bleeding to death."

Neither of us was squeamish at the sight of blood usually, but the amount of the crimson liquid oozing from my injured knee brought a look of horror to his face. His reaction was not what I had expected as his imagination seemed to get the better of him for a moment.

"Oh! Andy, I didn't mean to do that, 'onest mun," he blurted out.

"Run 'ome to your Mammy quick," he shouted.

I didn't need too much persuasion to follow that advice and hobbled homeward as quickly as I could. Soon Mammy was tearing at an old pillowcase, ripping lengths of the material and frantically wrapping them around my knee in an attempt to stem the flow of blood.

Normally she would have flown into a fit of temper when one of us had been daft enough to hurt ourselves, but today she was very concerned which, as she continued tearing at the pillowcase, was enough to make me think that the wound to my knee was indeed as bad as I had initially thought.

She must have laid at least four or five of the strips of bandaging on my knee and a further final strip used to tie the rest in place before the pillowcase was exhausted .

As the initial shock of the injury began to wear off, the pain became excruciating. My cries of Ow! Ow! Ow! had changed to a slobbering whimper as the whole scenario became more gruesome still. The blood seeping through the bandaging revealed itself as a growing crimson circle by the time Mammy stepped back and with a look of utter dismay on her face inspected her attempt at first aid. She was extremely concerned at my distress as I sat there with both hands clutched around my lower thigh in an attempt to stem the flow of blood and ease the searing pain. She decided there was no other option than to get me to Dr Nancy Evans.

So with me limping and being half carried by Mammy we made our way to the surgery where fortunately the doctor had finished her calls for the day. We were probably interrupting her much needed afternoon rest period but she didn't show any sign of irritation at our impromptu visit. She didn't even bother taking us into the surgery, but dealt with me there in her living room.

Ivy, the doctor's assistant and companion, placed a towel on one of the plush chairs opposite the doctor and sat me down with Mammy alongside. Then, after a quick glance at my knee, Dr Evans sprang into action. At the same time, in her usual brusque, but good natured manner, she even took the trouble to compliment Mammy on her crude first aid efforts.

"To be sure now, Mrs Swain you've done a good job in stemming the flow of blood. To be sure now."

I wasn't quite sure how to interpret the next compliment that this time she paid to me however. Particularly as it also seemed to send a secret signal to her assistant Ivy who then gently, but firmly, placed her strong hands on my shoulders.

"And Handel is a brave young lad I know – to be sure he is."

The last time she had said something like this was a few years before when I had a crack to my head and she had produced a little brown bottle containing the 'kill or cure' remedy – Iodine.

Sure enough, as she finished unravelling the bandaging, in one swift movement she picked up the little brown bottle and was deftly applying its contents to my wounded knee. The stinging sensation of the treatment was almost as bad as the cause of my injury. I could only wince as I did my utmost to stifle the heart rending cry in my throat. Ivy's hands gently tightened on my shoulders.

"There Mrs Swain, didn't I tell ye so. Handel is a brave boy."

Surprisingly, the flow of blood from the wound decreased dramatically. It was down to a slight trickle now as Dr Evans kept dabbing away with her Iodine soaked cotton wool pad, closely inspecting it before deciding what her next move should be.

It was then that Ivy, who had left the room for a moment, returned, presumably from the surgery. She gave the doctor what I can only describe as a length of catgut about three inches long. I wondered what on earth she was going to do with it. Then to my amazement, without any warning except once again the slight pressure of Ivy's hands on my shoulders, Dr Evans calmly began to pierce the flesh of my knee.

She pushed the needle drawing the catgut into one side of the wound then out through the other before gently twisting it and closing the wound. No anaesthetic was necessary, even if it had been available, as the shock to my nervous system was sufficient to freeze any impulses of pain my body might have wished to transmit to my brain. Finally the stitched-up wound was packed with cotton wool and lint while Ivy neatly finished off the job by applying real bandages.

I was off from school for a week as Dr Evans told Mammy that it would take that long for the wound to heal and for the stitch to be effective. Of course after Dinky had told practically everyone in the whole school precisely how I was injured – that we had been playing Cowboys and Indians at the time – on my return to school I was met with a barrage of name-calling.

Among them a favourite was Big Chief Broken Knee. It was weeks before I lived that one down.

CHAPTER 9

A new slant on postal romance

My injured knee only took a week to heal. Maggie's hurt on the other hand was an entirely different matter. In late April she suffered a broken heart as circumstances forced her and her beloved Sam apart. The time had come for him to do his National Service in the Royal Navy. To help bridge the gap that was to be created between them the pair made a pact that they would write to each other every day without fail.

Sometimes courting couples would write on the back of their love letters the initials SWALK – sealed with a loving kiss, or ITALY – I trust and love you, but not Maggie and Sam. Instead they came up with the romantic notion of sticking the postage stamp at a slight angle so that only they would know it was a letter from their true love. Maggie pinched this idea from a woman's magazine. It didn't seem to matter that they could tell whose letter it was from the handwriting or the fact that they never got letters from anybody else. Still it seemed to keep them happy.

Every day Maggie received a letter from Sam and every day she would point at the stamp, fixed at its special angle indicating that she knew who it was from, before disappearing upstairs to devour its messages of love. The Royal Navy was very active patrolling the seas of the world and I can't recall Sam ever coming home on leave, but that didn't seem to blunt their ardour and their love for each other remained strong throughout his absence. During this time I expect Maggie would have attracted the attention of many other men. She was a tall, very attractive young woman, but I can honestly say that unlike some of the other girls whose boyfriends were away, Maggie remained faithful.

Molly too was attracting male attention by this time. She was smaller in stature than Maggie. She had honey blonde hair and a ready smile with a much softer personality. She never lost that girlish sparkle or delight with life and her head was filled with dreams and romantic notions. Like me she was an avid reader and always had her head stuck in some book or other.

She loved magazines like Woman's Weekly, True Romance or Girls Crystal which were full of stories where the heroine eventually found her Prince. But her favourite stories were from the Arabian Nights and her heroine was Scheherazade – the narrator of the tales.

I'm sure that Molly felt her life was complete after we got the wireless and she discovered the beautiful haunting music of the same name. She wouldn't miss a performance for anything and encouraged me to listen. It was my introduction to classical music and for this I shall forever be in Molly's debt.

It was not surprising that Molly had many suitors, but none of them lasted long. She had set herself very high standards, based I expect, on

the heroes she had conjured up in her mind from the stories she read. I shall always remember one particular young man who came calling. There was nothing extraordinary or special about him except that he owned a motorcycle – a very powerful one. He must have been about eighteen or nineteen and a little on the small side with a lean frame and narrow shoulders. He wasn't at all the sort of person one would expect to be charging around on such a powerful machine. His name was Cedric and he lived in Sketty – one of the posh parts of town. His father was a client of the firm of solicitors that Molly then worked for and she had caught his eye when he visited their office. His next move had been to hang around outside her office pretending that it was a chance meeting so he could walk her to the bus stop. Within a matter of weeks Cedric had turned up on the motorcycle offering to give Molly a lift home.

Mammy had already warned her that under no circumstances was she to get involved with men riding motorbikes. It would have been very hard for her to resist the thrill of riding pillion since she would have been the envy of all the other girls in the neighbourhood. She probably told Cedric to drop her off at the end of the road so that Mammy wouldn't know.

Despite the fact that Molly had warned Cedric of Mammy's attitude to motorcyclists he soon took to roaring up and down the road outside our house most evenings and weekends. Molly pretended to ignore him and when Mammy asked if she knew this young hooligan creating the din she protested her innocence. That meant she couldn't venture outside as that would give the game away. Instead she sat by the window in the parlour with a book in her hands, secretly watching the antics of Cedric as he raced around the neighbourhood to impress her. It was fascinating to see this young man with his flat cap and plus fours trying to impress Molly.

One person who knew of Cedric's infatuation with Molly was Daniel. She couldn't keep the secret from him as his office was so close to hers and when she was swanning around on the motorbike she should have been coming home on the bus with him. Daniel and Molly had always been very close in the same way as I was to both of them. Molly knew that Daniel would never give the game away but he did confide in me.

Cedric's usual routine was to appear in the road outside our house between half past six and seven. He would stop by the lamp-post on the square and, propping the bike up with one leg, would shake the entire neighbourhood by revving the engine for a couple of minutes. He would then slowly circle the area giving the machine an occasional short burst of power. Daniel and I would sit on our garden wall with Molly at her usual station in the parlour window.

After this initial demonstration it was normal for him to suddenly shoot off down the hill, go tearing into the nearby warren of side streets before emerging once more on to the square. But on one fateful occasion disaster struck. He just kept circling the square, constantly revving up the engine before stopping and switching off. Mercifully, but briefly silence would reign. Then came the most disturbing part of the performance – kick-starting this brute of a machine once more. It always seemed reluctant to fire and took at least half-a-dozen attempts before coming alive.

Watching this puny young man bouncing up and down with one foot kicking down on the starting pedal and the other in the air was comical. For the best part of half-an-hour he kept stopping and starting, repeating this laborious task of kick-starting the machine. Then, as if the machine was angry with being abused in this way it decided to kick back. The machine burst into life alright, but instead of the pedal remaining down it sprang back with ferocious energy and catapulted poor Cedric onto the road. Finally, the motorbike, with one spiteful act of revenge, turned and fell on him before its engine finally spluttered and cut out.

Daniel and I both stood up, startled and shocked by Cedric's screams. He was sprawled on the road with the monster of a motorbike crushing down on him. I would have loved to have been in the parlour just to see how Molly had reacted. We were not the only people who had witnessed the accident. Fortunately for him Cedric's breach of the peace had attracted many neighbours, two of whom were now racing across to help. First to reach him was Mr Davies from next door.

"Daniel! Quick, run to the telephone box, dial 999 for an ambulance," he shouted to us after a quick inspection of Cedric.

For Daniel being part of this drama and having to phone the emergency services was a dream come true. We had seen this in the pictures and heard it on the wireless, but to be asked to do it in real life was unbelievable. He didn't wait to be told twice and was soon haring down to the nearest phone box with me on his heels. I had to see this for myself – Daniel dialling 999. I only just made it in time. As I got to the phone box Daniel was relaying the information to the operator. I felt so proud of him and thought it was a good job that it was my brother Daniel who had been given the task of ringing for the ambulance. He worked in an office and was used to telephones. Any other boy in the neighbourhood might not have known what to do.

We soon heard the alarm bells ringing in the distance as the ambulance speedily made its way to the scene of the accident. By the time we returned a crowd had gathered around Cedric. Some of the men had removed the motorcycle from on top of him and it was propped up in the middle of the square. Unlike Cedric the machine seemed to have come through the ordeal unscathed. Fortunately for him there were a lot of people there who, because of the needs of war, were well versed in first aid. Some women had wrapped him in blankets to keep him warm, while others offered words of comfort in an attempt to calm him. He was still in a considerable amount of pain as apart from constantly groaning he occasionally let out an anguished cry. Perhaps this was for the benefit of Molly, the object of his desire, who had unsympathetically failed to materialise though I bet her eyes were glued to the parlour window.

Mr Davies, who had been the first to attend to Cedric, stood a little apart from the crowd now quite content to let the women take over the care of the young man. Daniel and I went and stood next to him.

"Good work Daniel. You called the ambulance then – it'll be here soon," he said.

"Yes, Mr Davies," Daniel replied with a sense of pride.

"The bells are getting louder now."

Then, with a wink, Mr Davies asked Daniel almost in a whisper so that others wouldn't hear.

"This young sport chasing after your Molly, is he?"

He had caught Daniel off guard and for a moment he hesitated before answering – cleverly I thought.

"Oh, My mother wouldn't allow that Mr Davies. She wouldn't approve of Molly riding on a motorbike."

He had not lied. His answer of course was true. Mammy would not approve, but at the same time he was warning Mr Davies and hoping for Molly's sake that he would not repeat his thoughts to Mammy.

"Oh, no! Mr Davies. Molly would be in trouble if she was caught riding on a motorbike," he said, repeating his words, just to make sure.

Mr Davies just smiled and nodded, but remained silent. I think he'd got the message. How he knew about Molly and Cedric I never found out. He might have seen them on the motorbike or just put two and two together. Whether Mammy ever found out is another matter. Perhaps Mr Davies would have thought it was his duty to tell her. After all riding pillion on motorbikes was a dangerous pastime. Anyway Molly seemed to have escaped Mammy's wrath on this occasion as she never mentioned it. Perhaps she preferred to ignore her daughter's indiscretion now that Cedric had been put out of action for possibly several months until his wounds healed. More than likely his parents had also confiscated the powerful machine having seen their error in letting him have it in the first place.

The day of this incident was in fact the last time we saw Cedric or, as far as our neighbours were concerned, that was the last we heard of him and his motorbike. For safety's sake Mr Davies had taken the machine off the road and put it in his front garden after the accident. The following day two men came to collect it with a builder's lorry.

Daniel discovered some months later that Cedric, like most young men, had been called up for National Service.

As for Molly she didn't seem to care tuppence for Cedric or what became of him. Like the heroine in the books she read she was still waiting for her prince to come.

CHAPTER 10

Learning one of life's hard lessons

T he month of June 1947 will forever remain painfully etched in my memory. When it began I was filled with confidence and optimism. I was eagerly looking forward to the rapidly approaching day when I would prove worthy of Mammy's faith in me and justify her ambitious plans for my future. On that day I was going to sit the scholarship exam. No one, including myself, had any doubt that I was going to pass this and attend Swansea Grammar School. This was something that would open the door for greater achievements. I wasn't expecting to get as far as university – that would have been far too ambitious for a boy from the Hafod. Mammy had set her sights on the teacher training college. She wanted me to become a teacher.

Failing the examination never entered my mind. I was fortunate that I enjoyed learning. Schoolwork came easily to me whatever the subject, especially the three Rs in which I excelled. If I didn't come top of the class I was always in the first three, so it was a racing certainty that I was going to pass and with the coming of the new school year would be leaving Hafod School for good.

On the big day I woke to brilliant sunshine on a glorious, early summer morning. The examination was universal with pupils attending their own schools but with teachers from other schools acting as invigilators. Strangely on that day I had my first severe attack of what I now believe to be hay fever. It wasn't thought of as an allergy then and we always believed that a stuffy nose and watery eyes at this time in the year was the result of a summer cold.

Apart from the flowers and bowling green in the park not a lot of grass or pollen bearing plants grew in the Hafod, so hay fever was not a common occurrence. Anyway, by the time I arrived at school and took my place in the classroom my eyes were streaming. It was uncomfortable and a little disconcerting, but I was in no great pain and not unduly worried about taking the exam. After all I was on familiar territory, sitting in my own classroom, in my own school.

The young woman acting as invigilator seemed to recognise my problem instantly as she was soon wiping my eyes. She was even kind enough to let me borrow her handkerchief to keep my eyes and nose clear. So sitting the examination was not a problem. I coped with the hay fever well enough and was quite sure that I had answered the questions and completed the test paper without any problems, confident that I was going to pass.

Sadly this was not to be. Instead, when the results were announced some weeks later, before school broke up for the summer holidays, I had a shock. Just one boy in the whole of the school had passed. I was completely bewildered. My pride had taken a severe knock and I felt ashamed. I had let my family down – particularly Mammy – as well as the friends, neighbours and teachers who were convinced that I was a star pupil and bound to pass.

Somehow I felt that I had been cheated by this unexpected result, but at the time refrained from airing my thoughts for fear it might sound like sour grapes. The thing that puzzled me was that the one lad who did pass had never been the brightest boy in the class. True, he wasn't dull, but his success still mystified me. Why had he passed when others, with far better track records, had failed?

My hopes were temporarily resurrected when Mr Richards – Baldy – told me there would be places at Dynevor School which sometimes accepted borderline cases. This offered the possibility of sitting the matriculation examination and going on to higher education.

Surely, I thought, I would fall into this category and still be in with a chance that I could realise my ambition of becoming a teacher. Sadly it was not to be as just two boys were chosen from Hafod School – and I wasn't one of them. By now I was now totally bewildered. All of my hard work, my aptitude for learning, the encouragement of my family and teachers would count for nothing. My future looked bleak.

Failing that examination was a turning point. My hopes and dreams were shattered. My outlook on life, indeed my whole personality changed dramatically. I knew Mammy was disappointed. Like me she found it difficult to accept, that with all the promise I had shown and the encouraging reports from teachers, I had failed. Her hopes of having a son at grammar school had been dashed. She had kept our family together and endured where many would have failed and my success would have been her just reward.

Mammy was aware of how this unexpected occurrence was going to affect me, aware too that I felt ashamed and had let her down. She would have known that words would do little to solve the problem, but I remember well how she put a hand on my shoulder and tried her best to console me.

"Well Handel bach, this is a difficult time and you must be feeling sad," she said, before adding "But you must eat and drink, for life goes on and you just have to get on with it as best you can."

She hated self pity and this was her way of telling me that she would still give me her support, but she could not live my life for me. I had to pick myself up and deal with the problem.

Some weeks later during the summer holidays we were in town shopping for a pair of trousers. It was one of those rare occasions when Mammy was forced to buy me a new pair as there were no hand-me-downs. She had stopped to chat to a Mrs Thomas, an old acquaintance from town.

"Fitting him out with a new uniform for the grammar school are you?" said Mrs Thomas.

It was a casual enough remark, but for a moment I felt embarrassed and awkward, until Mammy answered her swiftly in a calm and straightforward manner.

"No, he didn't pass the scholarship Mrs Thomas. It is disappointing I know, but mind you he tried his best," she said.

"Well! There's sorry I am for you Handel," Mrs Thomas replied patting my head at the same time.

"I know you'd set your heart on going to the grammar school, didn't you boy?

Then the conversation took an unexpected twist.

"I bet there weren't many in his class who passed Mrs Swain," she continued, a note of cynicism in her voice.

"Poor Hafod children. They don't stand much of a chance."

Mammy's eyes narrowed as a quizzical look formed on her face.

"Well it's the same for everyone Mrs Thomas, isn't it? They all have an equal chance – don't they?" she asked.

It was Mrs Thomas's turn to narrow her eyes now.

"Don't you believe it, Mrs Swain," she said with conviction.

"Those places at the grammar school are already allocated mun. Before the exam begins even."

Mammy seemed perplexed.

"Do you think so Mrs Thomas? Surely not?" she inquired.

Mrs Thomas did very much think so.

"Oh we all know it down here, Mrs Swain. There's a lot of

skulduggery going on. You know, you scratch my back – and I'll look after your kids. It's the way of the world Mrs Swain.

"The children from better-off families and with connections will always be first in line for the favours that are going. We don't stand a chance Mrs Swain and especially you being a widow with seven children. That's their excuse see. They say that if they allow children like Handel from families like ours into the grammar school, how can you keep them there? Can you buy the uniform, the books and all the other extras that they need? And even if they do well, you'll bring them out as soon as its school leaving age to get them into work because you need the money. So that's their reasoning see – it would be a waste. Better to give the places in the grammar school to kids from well-off families who can afford to keep them there."

Mrs Thomas's speech seemed to hit a raw nerve with Mammy. She was a proud woman and had already demonstrated how willing she was to give her children every chance in life by arranging for Molly and Daniel to attend Gregg's College, a fee-paying school. Her anger showed as she replied.

"If what you say is true Mrs Thomas, then I would be very angry and upset indeed ," she said.

"No one can accuse me of not wanting and doing the best for my children. I am a widow as you say, with seven children, but four are working now. I would stand by and support Handel to ensure that the money was available for what ever he needed. Oh no! If that's their way of doing things then an injustice has been done to my family."

Mammy was getting very agitated which upset me and I think also upset Mrs Thomas too. I wondered whether she was just repeating gossip. Anyway she soon took her leave of us with a parting remark.

"Well never mind Mrs Swain, I'm sure that Handel will come through alright. Perhaps you'll send him to Gregg's like the other two," she said.

Thankfully those few words seemed to have a calming effect on Mammy, taking some of the sting out of the hurt she was feeling. But me? I was feeling more down than ever now. To think that I had been penalised just because I was from a poor and disadvantaged family! Mammy must have sensed this and as we continued walking towards the Co-op store where I was to get my new trousers she grasped my hand and delivered what she thought was the kind of reassuring message I wanted to hear.

"Yes, Handel bach, you'll go to Gregg's – like Daniel. And you'll get a good job too – you'll see," she said.

The thought of going to Gregg's and becoming a bookkeeper like Daniel didn't appeal to me. That was the last thing I wanted to do, but I refrained from saying anything. I realised that she was just trying to cheer me up and the thought that she was going to help me gave her new hope. She felt better now and there was a spring in her step again, but I felt more depressed than ever at the thought that the best thing on offer for my future was Gregg's College.

It was a hard lesson, a bitter pill to swallow.

CHAPTER 11

Climbing a rocky stairway to heaven

As the summer holidays drew to an end I seemed permanently enveloped by a feeling of melancholy. It was probably made worse by the fact that I was on my own. Dinky was once again away with his family visiting his grandparents in Weston-super-Mare and neither was there any sign of Brammer or Tommy Thomas.

A year had passed since our journey in search of the council rubbish dump. Our hunt for the elusive jam jars may have proved fruitless that day, but our trip had produced many plusses. We had discovered Llewellyn Park with its lake and island as well as the deep, dry, river bed leading up to it which had been colonised by the dreaded Japanese Knotweed – or German Rhubarb as we called it. Whenever we came across dense patches of the stuff we couldn't resist the challenge to take it on – and destroy it. In our minds it took on the mantle of the jungle and we instantly became the explorers we had seen in the cinema, hacking our way through it. There were also the fresh water springs that dotted the area, ideal for satisfying our raging thirsts after battling through the jungle. And of course there had been Erica, the weird posh girl who pretended she was a boy.

We had returned to Llewellyn Park many times since that first visit. Compared to Hafod Park with which we were more familiar, it was vast. Situated on the side of a hill the park rose gradually from the river to the lake. There, the land flattened out before rising again to the bowling green and tennis courts at the top. There was also a football pitch, albeit on a bit of a slope.

A large area of the park had been left as open grassland and at the furthest end was a small dense wood. We also discovered that the island in the centre of the lake could be accessed along a narrow strip of stepping stones hidden in the reeds. This would only be known to those who frequently used the park – like Erica. That was how she had managed to get onto the island and almost frightened us to death on the day of our first visit. We hadn't seen her since and because of the many distractions of the park we hadn't made it to the council rubbish dump either.

One day, with these thoughts in my head, I found myself taking the waters of the spring near St Peter's Church. Without the rest of the gang to distract me I was determined to find the dump and prepare the way for another expedition in the search for jam jars. If one was launched, perhaps we would even be able to make use of Mr Lewis's

wheelbarrow again – but this time with his permission. I had a fair idea of where the dump was. According to Erica I should continue along the road, past the cemetery and then beyond the park. I had no idea of what sort of distance was involved, but I was more determined than ever to find this elusive place.

Refreshed from drinking the cool spring water I hurried past the mortar works, quickening my pace to escape the ceaseless clanging of its machinery. The still, warm summer's afternoon seemed to exaggerate its deafening noise, but this soon became fainter and fainter as I left it behind.

The bridge dividing the roads was now in view and I thought I could just make out the shape of a lone figure sitting on the wall. It was probably wishful thinking, but I believed that it was Erica. I never found out because by the time I had reached the bridge the figure had disappeared. If it was her I wondered whether she had been aware that I was approaching and indeed if she had recognised me. Anyway whoever it was they had vanished. I consoled myself with the thought that it had probably just been my imagination.

As I passed the high cemetery walls, in the shade of the tall trees behind them, the warmth and sunlight faded. I began to wish I hadn't ventured on this journey on my own and had waited for another day when at least Dinky might have been with me.

I remembered our first visit to this place. The meeting with Erica remained clear as did the memory of how she had stalked and frightened us in the park, taken Brammer's cap and scared the wits out of us. Was she doing the same thing now I asked myself. Was she stealthily trailing me, perhaps even trying to scare me? I thought that would be fun, then I had different thoughts which prompted me to quicken my pace and look over my shoulder. What if I was being stalked, but not by Erica? My speedy walk developed into a quick trot and soon I was running full pelt, leaving the cemetery, park – and whatever else my imagination had conjured up – behind me.

When I eventually stopped, I found myself in completely new territory. The road curved gradually to the left, lined on that side by hedges enclosing fields. On my right was the river and across this were huge mounds, twenty to thirty feet high of some kind of blue-grey industrial waste. Forgetting about whoever I thought was after me and intrigued by this sight I crossed the shallow river to take a closer look at these strange mounds. I felt like an explorer in the books I had read, people like Alan Quartermain or George Edward Challenger, discovering a new Stonehenge or The Pyramids even.

When I got closer I scooped up some of the material which resembled ground up slate and let it trickle through my fingers. It seemed smooth and greasy, not the same consistency as the waste at Hafod tip. It had a similar colour to lead and I wondered whether there was once some ancient lead mine here. Then it struck me. Was this part of the elusive dump? Had this material been brought here from somewhere else? It seemed to be so out of place alongside the river in this quiet secluded place.

Filled with the feeling that I was in a strange new world I returned to the road and followed it around the bend. It ended in a large open area with more mounds. This time they were of cinders and ash mixed with bottles, tin cans, bones and other household rubbish. I had indeed discovered the council dump. It looked and smelt awful, toxic and acrid, to say the least. The spot was enclosed on three sides by a steep rock face. They were filling in an old quarry.

The place appeared yet to be discovered by the local seagull population. There were just a few crows and smaller birds picking over the rubbish. Copying them, I picked up what looked like an old stair rod and began poking into the nearest mound. I quickly found two one pound jam jars – or their remains that is – as both were broken. Not a good start, I thought. Harry had failed to mention when he talked about there being 'loads of jam jars up the dump' that most of them were in bits. It took another half an hour of probing and scraping at the mounds of rubbish before I was eventually rewarded with a solitary two pound jar that was intact. But my efforts were not entirely in vain as I also found two pop bottles and a beer flagon. There was money to be returned on these – a penny each.

I now needed somewhere to stash the booty until I could return with the rest of the gang – and hopefully Mr Lewis's wheelbarrow. To the right of the dump at the bottom of the rock face I could just make out a rock-strewn path which was almost completely covered with scrub and bramble. Crawling on my hands and knees I pushed my way in and emerged into yet another clearing which once again exposed hewn rock. I had discovered another, but much smaller, quarry. The place had a strange eerie atmosphere, like an isolated, silent world forgotten in time. This was where I would hide my haul. It took me two trips to get the bottles from the dump and hide them safely there. I felt pleased. The gang would be proud of me.

Then as I was about to make my way back to the dump for more, something frightened the life out of me – I wasn't alone after all. There was a sound coming from behind me. It was the sound of someone giggling. It was just so unexpected in a place that until then had been so still and quiet. I turned quickly and looked back, but could see no one. There were large chunks of rock strewn about the floor of the quarry mixed with bramble and gorse bushes. The giggling came again, high–pitched and squeaky. I recovered my composure and my instinct told me that this had the hallmark of someone I knew – the girl who thought she was a boy. Once again I was being stalked by Erica.

"I know it's you Erica. Been following me 'ave you?" I called out with a grin on my face.

She knew her little game was over and stood up from behind one of the rocks some twenty feet away.

"Oh, Andy. How nice – you remembered me!" she exclaimed with a surprised look on her face.

"How could anyone ever forget you, Erica?" I replied, more surprised by the fact that she had actually remembered me – and my name, but I didn't have any time to dwell on this fact as she began asking questions.

"Why are you all alone Andy? Where are your friends – Dinky Brammer and Thomas?" she inquired.

She was as confident as when we had first met and immediately I felt a little intimidated by her. It was a class thing. She was posh and even by working class standards I was from a poor family. Under normal circumstances we would probably never have met, let alone become friends. Her family would have seen to that.

All of these negative thoughts were swirling about in my head as I hesitatingly replied, selecting my words carefully and remembering to pronounce my aitches.

"Oh they're away – gone on holiday they have – visiting."

"Well I am glad Andy, and very much relieved too that you are alone," she replied to my surprise.

I knew that her attitude was a little prissy and she spoke a bit like a schoolmistress, but she seemed an honest individual and I liked her.

93

Anyway I thought I would play safe – I was on my own without the rest of the gang to back me up and this was her territory. Erica then proceeded to tell me why she was glad that I was on my own.

"This is a special place, my secret hideaway," she said, sweeping her arms around the quarry.

"No-one knows of this place but me," she added.

She hesitated for a moment, took a deep breath and, pointing a finger at me, said "Until today of course, when, clever boy that you are, you discovered it Andy."

"I must accept this Andy and I really don't mind as long as you keep it a secret too," she added after taking another deep breath.

Then, changing her tone, she started pleading with me.

"Please say you will Andy. Promise me. Let this haven be for us only – our special place."

The quarry obviously meant a lot to her, a special secret haven as she called it. I was only too willing to make that promise, particularly when she offered a kind of trade-off.

"If you will then I'll show you a place even better than this. The most special place of all."

A place more secret than this? The prospect intrigued me and I nodded, agreeing to her terms.

"Of course I'll keep it a secret Erica. I won't even tell Dinky – and e's my best friend."

I had quickly forgotten about pronouncing my aitches, but it didn't seem to matter now. We had a common bond between us – the secret quarry.

Her joy at my words was overwhelming and she began skipping in and out of the rocks and boulders on the quarry floor chanting as she did so.

"Our secret place, Andy. Our secret place"

She must have repeated the words a dozen times before she stopped and ran to the bottom of the rock face.

"Follow me Andy, follow me – to the most secret place of all," she invited in an irresistible fashion.

I could hardly believe my eyes as she began climbing what appeared to be a twenty five to thirty foot sheer rock face. She was as agile as a monkey, finding ledges and footholds for her hands and feet with ease. Soon she was looking down at me from a shelf of rock about six feet from the top. She had her hands on her hips and a proud and determined look in her eyes. She didn't say anything. There was no need. She had thrown down the gauntlet.

By her action Erica had proved that she was as good and brave as any boy, but the most daring part of her already amazing ascent up the cliff was yet to come. I failed to see just how she was going to complete the climb and reach the top as the shelf of rock on which she was standing was covered by a craggy overhang.

When she did make her next move I gasped in amazement. To her right, and protruding from the soil at the top of the cliff was the trunk of a stunted oak tree. It had several sturdy branches, one of which curved down to within about three feet of where she stood. I thought there was no way that she could reach it, but this incredible girl was full of shocks and surprises. As if to reassure me she waved her hand before launching her lithe, slim body out and upwards aiming for the branch – the only thing between her and certain death. I wanted to close my eyes, but I dare not.

For a moment she seemed to hang in space and I expected to see her come crashing down onto the boulder-strewn floor below, but she made it with ease, clinging to the branch and pulling herself on to the tree trunk then up to the top. She stood up and with a look of triumph on her face challenged me to follow her.

"Come on Andy you can do it," she said.

Thinking about it was not going to help. I knew I had to follow her if I wanted to keep her respect. I ran to the bottom of the rock face, believing as I got closer that the climb was not going to be as difficult as it looked from a distance. I had often shinned up walls steeper than this with fewer hand and footholds, though not as high. The bit that still had me worried though was the final six feet, but there was no pulling out now.

I kidded myself that, like the rock face the jump would not be so bad once I was up there. I was wrong – it was worse.

The first part of the climb went well as I reached the shelf under the overhang and pulled myself onto it. It was over a yard long and a few feet wide. I sat there with my back pressed against the cliff gazing into space. I felt compelled to look down and for the first time in my life I experienced a strange whirling sensation that filled me with nausea, paralysing my body and mind. It was vertigo. Erica quickly realised, probably by the look of fright and desperation on my face, that I was in trouble. Without raising her voice and showing no sign of alarm she softly called out to me.

"Andy! Don't think about it. Stand up now and jump for the tree."

Whether it was her calm words or just sheer terror spurring me on, I don't know, but without stopping to think and in one panic-led movement I leapt from the rock shelf, grabbed the branch and scrambled onto the tree trunk. Then with all the strength I could muster I pulled my shaking body off the tree and up onto the top of the cliff. I fell to the ground where I lay, eyes closed and face down, for the next few minutes. I needed the reassurance of feeling the earth beneath me.

Erica seemed to understand my reluctance to speak or move, perhaps she had felt the same way the first time she had completed the climb. She just sat beside me putting her hand on my shoulder and patting me gently. The late afternoon sun was warm on my back helping to soothe my shocked body and mind and with Erica's comforting presence I was content to remain sprawled there on the ground for the remainder of the day. But she was not going to allow too much time for me to wallow in this state of calm. She was eager to show off this special place – once hers alone, now ours and shared. Her gentle patting changed to firm shaking as she encouraged me to get up and inspect the spot that we had cheated death to reach.

"Come on Andy! Sit up and look at the view," she said. "You can see right over the town, all the way to the sea and the horizon."

Climbing the cliff had drained me of energy, but reluctantly I sat up, turned and looked in the direction that she was pointing. The town and the sea were familiar sights, but I had never before seen them as I did then. It was a breathtaking, truly remarkable sight. The sun was hovering over the glittering sea, the buildings of the town in front showing off the prominent Guildhall clock tower. All this was framed in the hills leading down the valley towards Swansea. For the first time in my life I was seeing the beautiful, natural setting of the place where I lived, away from the stark factories, mills, railways and slag heaps that were more familiar to me.

Taking a closer look at this special place where we were perched revealed that we were on a thin plateau covered with coarse grass overlooking the sheer cliff we had just scaled. On the other side the ground sloped down quite steeply through a tangle of scrub and gorse to the stream below. Beyond this there was a small wood or copse then farmland with some sheep and cattle grazing. Erica's secret hideaway, although high up and exposed with the quarry's steep rock face on one side and this extremely rough terrain on the other, was not a place to be easily discovered. But for those with courage – and Erica certainly had plenty of that – the stunning view over the town to the sea was a worthy reward. She laid back in the long grass secure in the knowledge that I approved. I was glad that I had taken the risk and followed her on this rocky stairway to heaven.

"Remember Andy," she whispered.

"This is our secret place – for you and me only."

Her eyes were closed and I watched her, studying her small, pale, oval face and her long skinny body and legs. She looked awkward and spindly, but that was far from the truth I knew. She was as agile and nimble as a monkey when she climbed up the quarry rock face.

It was with this picture framed , as I closed my eyes and lay down beside her. Then, immediately shot back up again as, with some trepidation I suddenly realised – how were we going to get back down.

"Andy! What is it?" exclaimed Erica as she too sat up, obviously surprised by my sudden movement.

Her bright brown eyes, wide with concern, were searching mine. I had already proved my courage and valour that day, but I was not going to push my luck any further. I had to be honest with her.

"I'm not going down the way we came up," I protested – defensibly maybe – but firmly.

To my great relief she appeared to understand my fear.

"I don't think even Tarzan would attempt that Andy," she said as she stood up. Then, taking hold of my hand, she helped me up and gave me some good news.

"Follow me and I'll show you the way down," she instructed.

Carefully she began picking her way down the steep slope through a tangle of gorse and scrub which led to the stream at the bottom. She was so light on her feet and with the gym shoes she had on she hardly disturbed the stony ground beneath her. I on the other hand found it nearly impossible to keep my balance as I slipped and slithered my way behind her in my hobnail boots, making the final descent on my backside. Erica didn't wait but continued walking until she reached the stream. We couldn't really see more than a couple of yards ahead as the stream was sheltered on both sides by overhanging trees and bushes. This didn't deter her as she daintily stepped from stone to stone with me clumsily following and, unlike her, getting my feet wet.

Soon we emerged into the open, near the great mounds of waste I had discovered earlier. We sat and rested here for a while and I explained to Erica my theory that these looked like the workings from an old lead mine. Very politely she begged to differ. Her theory was that it was rubbish that had been burnt and then dumped there.

As usual she spoke with such authority that I accepted what she said, but secretly I preferred my version of a Roman lead mine. We rejoined the road and strolled along leisurely with Erica almost reducing our pace to a crawl. All too soon we were passing beneath the shade of the high cemetery walls, very near to where she lived and I sensed that she did not want the day and our time together to end. I had discovered her special place and scaled the quarry heights. I had begun to harbour romantic notions that we would often meet repeating the adventure of today, but then she dropped a bombshell.

"I'm going away Andy, to Cheltenham and boarding school."

Her words stunned me. Today had been special. Although she was not a pretty girl she was not unattractive either. There was this bond between us now – the quarry and the challenge of scaling the rock face. I felt disappointed. My face and probably the whole of my demeanour must have reflected these thoughts.

"I'm so glad we met today Andy and that you discovered the old quarry. It will always be our special place," said Erica as we reached the cemetery gates and the parting of our ways where I discovered another of her quirky little traits – she hated goodbyes.

Without any warning she was off, running up the hill. She only stopped when she was at the gate of the large house where she lived where she turned and waved.

"In the spring, Andy," she called. "Look out for me in the spring."

CHAPTER 12

Boots not fit to kick a football

For the first time in my life the thought of returning to school didn't appeal to me in September 1947. The summer holidays were over and I was heading for a further period at Hafod School. This was not supposed to happen. It was not part of the big plan that I had set out for myself. Instead I should have been wearing a red jacket and matching cap, catching the bus for Swansea with a satchel-full of books slung over my shoulder. Sadly, that was to remain in my daydreams. The harsh reality was very different. This was a very dark period in my young life and I can clearly remember the feeling of desolation, but little of the actual events of the time. Like a chrysalis I had developed a hard shell of resentment, not knowing when it would crack for life to blossom once more. I was eleven and a half years old and I felt my life was in ruins.

Walter and Eddie were also in the boys' school now, but I can't remember ever seeing them. It seemed to be an unwritten rule that you never played with your siblings. Each class had its own designated area in the playground, laid down through time and custom by the generation of boys that had gone before. There were no visual lines of demarcation but each class had its own patch and everyone knew their place. A foolhardy youngster trespassing in the domain of an older class would quickly be welcomed with a boot up his backside. School dinners were being served now and because Mammy was a war widow we qualified for two free meals daily. These were allocated to the two youngest members of the family, in our case Walter and Eddie. Walter was being stubborn and was having none of this. He insisted on going home every dinnertime and Mammy would have to cook him his favourite dish – fried potato scallops. Mammy, the dinner ladies and the teachers all tried their best to get him to try the school dinners. They encouraged, cajoled, and even threatened him, but their efforts were to no avail. They even enlisted the help of the headmaster, Mr Joe Morgan, a formidable character, but even he had to admit defeat at the hands of this scrawny and obdurate nine-year-old boy.

However the free school dinner was not lost to the family as Mr Morgan agreed that I could have it instead. But that didn't really help Mammy. She still needed me home on a dinnertime as there were usually messages for me to run. I wasn't fussy and finicky with my food, I would eat whatever was put on the table for me, whereas Walter insisted on having his fried potato scallops. This meant that I bolted down my school dinner as quickly as I could before tearing off home. Luckily the dinner ladies and teachers did their very best to accommodate me and usually I was first in line to be served.

As always the weekend brought with it a mixture of distractions. Among them the Swansea Schools' Football League which had been reinstated after the war and as a result Saturday mornings were quite exciting. There would be a major exodus of schoolboys from the Hafod to support the school's teams at various parks in the area blessed with football pitches. Unfortunately at that time the pitch at Hafod Park with its uneven playing surface of ash and clinker was not

considered to be suitable. We thought this was a shame as it would have definitely given us a distinct advantage over the other school teams who were used to playing on flat, grass covered pitches, but until they brought the surface at Hafod Park up to scratch, our teams had to play home games at Cwmbwrla Park which was a couple of miles away.

I could kick a ball reasonably well and there were plans to form a junior team which I believed I had an outside chance of getting into. For a while it helped to lift my sense of doom and despair, but my hopes were soon dashed once more.

I was picked to play for the team but sadly I was not allowed to play as I didn't possess the necessary football boots. Hobnail boots, the only boots I had, were not allowed on the football pitch. The authorities believed that they could cause serious injury. I couldn't see how as most of the boys in our school had always played football in hobnail boots in the playground and I couldn't recall anyone suffering from serious injury. So that was it. I thought the world was conspiring against me once again. It seemed I was to be denied achieving anything in life that I either aspired to or cherished.

This dismal state of mind remained with me almost constantly. I was convinced 1947 was not a good year for me and the sooner it was gone and forgotten the better life would be. The year had started with one of the coldest winters on record and the chill winds that blew then, seemed to signal the bleak and harsh events that followed for me personally during the rest of the year.

Christmas, with all the magic it brought, did however make amends at least in part for all the bitterness and sorrow I felt I had suffered. Not only did I finally receive a pair of football boots as a gift, but with them came the rest of kit: jersey, shorts, socks and even shin guards. I couldn't have been more delighted. It was undoubtedly the best Christmas present I had ever had in my life.

Santa Claus had arrived in the guise of my brother Daniel. He was so incensed when he discovered that a lack of football boots prevented me from playing for the school team, he determined that somehow, he would get some for me. At the time he was working as a trainee bookkeeper with a firm of auctioneers in Swansea and as luck would have it a bag of goodies containing the football kit turned up in their salesroom. When Daniel informed the manager of my predicament he arranged for Daniel to buy them at an affordable price. However to raise even that amount of cash meant that for some time Daniel had to walk the two miles to his office and back every day thereby saving his bus fare. He was a quiet and unpretentious boy, but this act of kindness revealed his resilient and determined character. For me this unselfish attitude was justly rewarded when he too received an exceptional Christmas present that year. This also turned up in the sales rooms. With Mammy's help and no doubt that of the manager there he secured an almost new Raleigh bicycle. It came with three-speed gears and better still was equipped with an electric dynamo which provided power for the lights, saving on the cost of batteries.

So the year ended on a much brighter note with things taking a turn for the better. But I was still glad to see the end of 1947. It was a year that had changed my entire perception of life. It didn't seem as straightforward now and nothing seemed certain any more.

My dreams of the future were not so rosy either. With the coming of the New Year I would be 12. I was becoming a little more cynical and developing a day-by-day attitude to life.

I was growing up.

CHAPTER 13

Chaos and confusion in the classroom

In addition to all the upset and trauma I was experiencing in my own little world, the New Year of 1948 brought with it major changes in the whole structure of elementary education. The school leaving age was raised from fourteen to fifteen and the start of the school year switched from January to September. As a result, for the best part of the year the education system was thrown into a state of chaos and confusion. Somehow there seemed to be a need for special classes to be arranged, with children of various ages being placed together in preparation for the day when the new classes would be formed. A new teacher, Mr Eustace, took over standard five. Charlie Lewis who was also deputy head moved to standard six and Titus Thomas to standard seven. The changes also meant the creation of a new class – standard eight – to accommodate the 14 and 15 year olds. This was in the charge of Pet Summers.

I believe that this was Mr Eustace's first teaching post, coming into the profession as a young recruit direct from his wartime service in the Army. It was to his class that I was assigned on my first day back at school and, unfortunately for me, I was to gain the unenviable distinction of testing the cane he had acquired that very same day. It only amounted to one sharp rap across the palm of my hand and probably because it was the first time he used the cane, like me he never forgot the event. It came about because my whole attitude to life was changing. Regrettably I was becoming a little surly and cheeky. The class was assembled in the usual fashion of four to five rows with five desks in a row with two boys to a desk. I was sitting at the second desk of the first row when Mr Eustace decided that he would ask each boy in turn his full name and date of birth. He seemed very pleasant, fresh-faced and youthful with an easy-going manner – so much different to the other, older teachers. So when it came to my turn to reel off my details I inexplicably decided to put him to the test.

"And your name my boy," he asked.

"Handel Swain, Sir," I replied. "30th of January 1936."

Then as he was writing this into his notebook, for some unknown reason, I took leave of my senses.

"Oh, In front of my name, Sir, you can put the word The."

His expression didn't falter. He maintained the smile on his face.

"Oh, is that right," he said.

"Well my boy, come right out here and let's see how you feel about this then."

With that he picked up his brand new length of sugarcane, gave it a few practice swishes through the air and, with increasingly wobbly knees, I walked towards him.

That was our first encounter with Mr Eustace. Young and fresh-faced as he might have appeared, he had shown that he was not to be taken lightly and would demand the same respect as his older and more experienced colleagues. This showing of respect was of course a two-way thing. I had been disrespectful to him and had been punished accordingly. But that was it, the end of the matter. There was no resentment on my part and no grudges held by him. In fact Mr Eustace turned out to be an excellent teacher and very approachable. After that initial encounter my relationship with him could only get better. He encouraged his class and indeed all of the boys in the school to get involved in as much sporting activity as possible. Although he was mainly responsible for the football and cricket teams, he encouraged boys who were not particularly good at these two games into other sports such as bowls and athletics.

Hafod Park had an excellent bowling green which was well supported by the local men who jealously tended and guarded this prized square of turf. So it was quite an achievement on Mr Eustace's part when he succeeded in persuading them to allow the boys some use of the green. It must have come as quite a shock to other parks and bowling clubs in Swansea when they learned that their precious game, previously the preserve of middle aged and older men, was now being played by ten and eleven year-old boys.

Indirectly it might even have helped Dinky in his relationship with his father. Mr Miles was an ardent bowler and at first like most of the men, frowned upon the thought of sharing their beloved green with their sons. But as the boys became more proficient their fathers grew more interested and in many cases even began encouraging their offspring. It was a question of pride I expect, as the boy's ability to play the game would reflect upon the father.

Dinky turned out to be quite good at the game. His co-ordination was pretty sharp and, I must admit, I was no match for him. He was really too small to be of any use on the football field but at bowls he simply excelled. He took great delight in rubbing my nose in it as this was one of the few games in which he could beat me. But it still had the bonus as far as I was concerned that he always insisted that I played with him even when his father joined in. Boys whose fathers played bowls had a distinct advantage over those who did not. So for these times at least Mr Miles became like a surrogate father to me. He was still an extremely gruff and stern man, but he was beginning to mellow a little. I realised later that this change was not just down to playing a game of bowls with his son and me.

Things were stirring in Dinky's house. I noticed that a woman wearing a distinctly black or navy blue uniform with a matching hat, stockings and sturdy shoes was now becoming a regular visitor. Perhaps the most notable thing about this lady was the imposing leather case that she carried. We all knew just what she had in it, what she delivered to the ladies of the houses that she visited – babies! Of this we were certain. We couldn't fathom out just how the babies got into the case or where she got them from, but we knew that she delivered babies. All the women talked openly about it. Whenever there was a baby due this lady dressed in black delivered them.

There were other more vague suggestions made as to where the babies came from. There was an abundance of them around since the men had returned from the war so we guessed it probably had something to do with them. There was little or no sex education in schools in those days. It was also a taboo subject as far as most families were concerned. Still the arrival that summer of Gwladys, or Gladdy as she quickly became nicknamed, seemed to have a soothing effect on Mr Miles and a modicum of calm returned to the household.

The legacy of the war – of husbands and wives been separated for long periods of time – created havoc in their lives and the healing process took many years.

CHAPTER 14

Facing up to a personal challenge

Whatever else 1948 brought to my life, one thing that stood out was the shake-up that the education system underwent and what it meant for Hafod School. There were many changes during that year and when the term began in September new classes were formed. The seven to eleven year-olds were designated Junior One to Junior Four and the eleven to fifteen year-olds Senior One to Senior Four. Under this system I had to transfer from the old standard five, now S1 to the old standard six which was S2.

The most exciting and innovative change for me was the headmaster's plan to introduce an element of competition into school life. Classes were to be split into four sections and named after the colours red, blue, yellow and green. Each section had its share of bright boys and the not so bright and would be led by a captain and vice-captain. These titles had to be earned and were awarded purely on merit.

At the beginning of the school year examinations were held with the four boys scoring the highest marks appointed as captains and the next four as vice captains. They sat at the head of the class which was at the back then sloping down in order to the not so bright boys at the front. This was a reversal of the old system where the bright boys sat at the front and the not so bright at the back. Badges in the four colours were issued which were to be worn at all times when attending school.

This system gave the school a whole new impetus as each and every boy was now part of a team and wore his badge with pride. It was of particular interest to me. I had lost my way a bit since failing the scholarship. Any incentive to learn and do my best had diminished considerably. But now I had something to aim for once again.

I was always competitive and I didn't want just an ordinary badge or even a vice-captain's badge. I wanted my badge to be emblazoned with the word Captain. I soon realised I was going to have to work hard to earn that for things were different now. In previous years, because I was born in January, I was one of the older boys. Now I found myself in a class where around a third of my fellow pupils were older than me. The age difference wasn't a problem, as it was, at the most, just a matter of a few months, but I had no idea of the competition these older boys would provide. Anyway I pulled out all the stops and when the final results were announced I was delighted to scrape home in fourth place – I was captain of the green team.

Winning the captain's badge had meant a great deal to me. I felt that I had regained my self-esteem and the respect of my classmates and teachers once more. On the whole, things went extremely well and I fitted in comfortably with my new classmates with the exception of William Jones – or Will-ho as he was known.

Will-ho's family had moved down into the Hafod from the top of the Swansea Valley where, if Will-ho was anyone to go by they had the peculiar trait of tagging on the phrase 'ho' to everyone's name. As far as he was concerned my name was now 'andel-ho; Dinky became Dinky-ho; Brammer, Brammer-ho and Tommy, Tommy-ho.

At first it was a bit disconcerting that whenever he spotted me, in the street, the school yard or in the park I would be greeted with a shout of 'andel-ho. I soon grew used to this and didn't particularly mind as there were many boys in the school with far worse nicknames than that – Mangie, Ummer, Smelly and Bladder to name just a few. These names were given to the boys when they were very young and they just grew up with them. There was no malice attached, so no one really minded.

Apart from attaching 'ho' to the end of peoples names, Will-ho had one other very nasty habit and, for reasons that became apparent later, he selected me as a potential victim. It was a bit unnerving when he first began to hang around me, getting as close as he could and putting me under close scrutiny. He was not a particularly big lad, but broad-shouldered and thick set. He was wild looking with a shock of spiky, fair hair, a pale complexion and large round blue eyes. Yet for all the attention that I was getting from him he never looked me straight in the eye. So in that respect his unwelcome attention was not in any way threatening but unnerving to say the least.

At first I couldn't make out what it was about me that fascinated him, but I was soon to find out and in a rather uncomfortable and painful way. Things came to a head one fine, late autumn day. I was sitting on the school perimeter wall soaking up the morning sun waiting for Dinky to turn up. Suddenly Will-ho appeared. Catching me by surprise, he stood in front of me blocking out the sun.

"Blackheads,'andel-ho, blackheads! Keep still, Keep still," he uttered encouraging me not to move a muscle.

With that, his thumbs protruding, he began digging into my nose and squeezing hard. I just couldn't believe what was happening. I was petrified. Frozen to the spot. I thought for a moment that I was being attacked by some horrible creepy-crawly insects. He seemed possessed and kept squeezing my nose continuing to shout at me.

"Black'eads! Black'eads! Let me get the black'eads out."

Finally, with my eyes watering and my head spinning from the pressure he was putting on my nose, I managed to get up and push him away from me.

"Gerroff mun Will-ho. Are you daft mun. What you doin'?"

Whatever these blackheads were and whatever they were doing I decided that the cure was worse than the ailment. His reaction to my sudden rebuttal of his unwelcome attention wasn't what I expected. He stood there with his hands held before him and thumbs still protruding. He looked hurt and annoyed as he pushed his thumbs towards me once again.

"Look mun 'andel-ho, look at the black'eads I got out of your nose," he said.

My first thought was to run away from him as fast and as far as possible, but my curiosity got the better of me. I'd never heard of these black'eads so I scrutinised his dirty thumbnails searching for them.

"Where's the cowin' black'eads?" I screamed back at him. "I can't see anything."

And that was the truth. No matter how closely I looked there didn't seem to be anything visible on his fingers. But he persisted.

"Aye mun," he said. "Gimme your 'and and I'll give 'em to you."

Before I had time to think, he grabbed my hand and wiped the rim of one thumbnail across my palm – then performed the same act with the other. And there were his precious blackheads, reduced now to two dirty smears of grease. Triumphantly he pointed at them with a note of great satisfaction in his voice.

"There see 'andel-ho. Black'eads. You've got to get 'em out mun."

He then proceeded to give me a sermon on the necessity of removing all blackheads from the face of the earth. It seems it had been drummed into him by his mother and three older sisters who were constantly on the lookout for blackheads, to the extent of involving Will-ho in giving them a quick check after their weekly baths and removing any signs of the offending spots.

Of course the three sisters gladly reciprocated to ensure that Will-ho himself was blackhead free. Urged on by his three older sisters he had a mission in life – to free the planet of the offending blemishes. He made me promise that when I got home after school I would

complete the job he'd started. Needless to say after this strange encounter with Will-ho I kept a safe distance from him just in case the irresistible urge to start attacking my nose again came upon him .

Until I had met Will-ho I wasn't aware that the things existed or that I even had them, but the thought of these blackheads lodging in my nose preyed on my mind for the rest of the day. With some apprehension and trepidation, I locked myself in the bathroom that evening and stood in front of the mirror, with the sole purpose of inspecting my nose and eradicating these dreadful things.

This was the first time that I ever paid close scrutiny to any part of my body. But after close inspection of my face I could clearly see what Will-ho was getting so agitated about. For running across the bridge of my nose was a distinct line of greasy and enlarged pores; which had been brought about undoubtedly by the constant removal of mucus by the quickest and most convenient method – which all boys used then – a swift and firm wipe of the coat sleeve.

Handkerchiefs, I'm sorry to say, were not an essential part of a Hafod schoolboy's normal kit. The predominant use of the schoolboys' sleeve in place of the handkerchief also resulted in it acquiring a shiny hue or the silver-sleeve as it became known.

Anyway twenty minutes later, after some banging on the bathroom door by various members of the family desperate to use it's facilities, I emerged blackhead free, but with my nose resembling the look and texture of a strawberry. It must have taken all of two hours for the now tortured skin on my nose to calm down during which time I drew some very caustic comments from Harry.

"What 'ave you been doing 'andel? Your nose looks like a squashed tomato," he said more than once.

The one good thing that did come out of my brush with Will-ho and the discovery of the dreaded blackheads, was that I paid a bit more attention to my personal hygiene.

Mammy could not afford to buy handkerchiefs but she always kept a good supply of clean cloths salvaged from old bed linen pillowcases and clothing. In fact anything that could be used in place of handkerchiefs or bandages.

With time and a lot of self-discipline I developed the habit of using a piece of clean rag as a nose-wipe instead of the sleeve of my jacket. I also kept a close watch on my nose and indeed all of my face. And

I would immediately spring into action squeezing with thumbs and fingers at the first sign of anything resembling a blackhead.

The last thing I wanted was to come under close scrutiny from Will-ho again who I suspect would have unflinchingly launched another attack on my unsuspecting nose.

CHAPTER 15

Hello Sid and goodbye Maggie

Despite all the upheaval that 1948 had brought me personally, there was one member of the Swain family whose future was looking extremely rosy as Christmas approached. That was Maggie. Her fiancé as she now liked to call her boyfriend Sam had completed his National Service and resumed work in the town's ship repair yard. Great plans were being laid for their forthcoming marriage at St John's Church. It was to be a white wedding with Daniel giving Maggie away and Molly acting as a bridesmaid. With nearly all of Mammy's time and attention taken over by this it was a wonder that she managed to prepare for the coming festive season at all.

It was during this hectic period that we first met Sid, a short, scrawny young man with dark, wavy hair and thin pallid features. However, he more than made up for this lack of stature with his boisterous and infectious personality. He always had a wide grin on his face, but perhaps his greatest asset, his trump card, was that he could do the jitterbug. This meant he was a big hit with the girls and always in great demand on the dance floor. It was at the local dance, the Friday night hop at the Parish hall, where he first met Molly.

Well they say that love is blind and that beauty is in the eye of the beholder, which must have been the case when Molly met Sid. As physically at least he didn't come anywhere near to being the Prince Charming that Molly had dreamed of. He wore a double-breasted suit, a trilby hat and walked with a definite swagger. I believed he was trying to give the impression that he was some sort of poor man's Dick Tracy. But he was good fun and made us all laugh which was very different to Maggie's boyfriend Sam who was rather quiet and a little on the sober side.

Sid's courtship of Molly was ardent and stubborn. He knew that she was a prize catch as she was an extremely pretty and well-educated young woman with many suitors. She could take her pick of young men from good backgrounds with good jobs and Sid was certainly at a disadvantage in this respect. Like us he was from a relatively poor family and although he didn't seem short of cash, his job as a window cleaner did not inspire much confidence for the future. Especially when Mammy found out. She spelled it out to Molly in no uncertain terms that, she should never contemplate having a steady relationship with a man whose ambition rose no higher than being a window cleaner. I remember her laying it firmly on the line to Molly.

"Sid might be a nice young man Molly, but you can't start courting or even think about marrying him. He's a window cleaner! It's not a proper job."

She kept emphasising this over the days that followed.

"He must have a proper job. You can tell him that he's not welcome here until he gets himself – a proper job."

Now Molly was quietly determined too and Sid, with all his faults, was the one young man that she wanted. So within a couple of weeks of having the law laid down she proudly announced "I told Sid what you said Mammy – about him getting a proper job. Well he starts next Monday with the South Wales Transport. He's going to be a conductor on the busses."

And sure enough the following Monday, after he had completed his first shift of ringing the bell and collecting the money on the buses, Sid presented himself before us in his full bus conductor regalia including the leather money bag which he carried over his shoulder. He now had a proper job as far as Mammy was concerned and she gladly welcomed him into the Swain household.

Sid fitted in very well with our family especially with Walter Eddie and me. He was always fooling around, making us laugh and could invariably lay his hands on a bag of sweets or some nuts which he would share with us. He also knew that it was in his best interests to keep on the right side of Mammy and surprised us all one day when he volunteered to do the ironing.

Like most young men Sid had done his stint of National Service and had become a dab hand with an iron. In fact he was quite proud of the razor-sharp creases he could get on any old pair of trousers. Mammy laughed when he first volunteered, but he persisted and showed her just how competent he was. So she let him get on with it.

Once a week, on a Tuesday, when the clothes which had been washed on the Monday were dry and ready to be ironed, Mammy would trot off to the Manor cinema while Sid got on with the ironing. This was really some feat as the flat iron had to be constantly heated over the open fire. I can still picture him in my mind as he tested that the iron was the right temperature by spitting on it and if this sizzled to the right tune it was ready. Of course the added bonus for Sid was with Mammy away at the cinema he had Molly all to himself, and it was easy for him to get rid of us boys for half-an-hour with the welcome bribe of a few nuts or sweets.

Strangely though, Harry seemed to favour Maggie's boyfriend. The quieter, more sober Sam. Their personalities were as different as night from day but they seemed to bond well. One of their common interests was watching the Swans play. Sam was a keen football fan. He had played the game well as a schoolboy but after leaving school confined his passion for the game to watching it. Just as strangely, until he met Sam, Harry had shown no interest in the game. After the last troubling episode when he had got involved with the odious Issy Smith and the theft of the money from Issy's mother's bag he had managed to stay out of serious trouble. I believe he finally realised that the threat of ending up in borstal or an approved school could come true. Since then he had also left school behind and for most of the time now he was working.

Mammy was only too aware that keeping Harry's mind and hands occupied through hard physical work kept him out of trouble. So she was extremely glad when he struck up a friendship with Tom 'the car' who, like Harry, was also working at the copperworks. Tom was never far away from his car. He seemed to spend all of his spare time stripping it down and rebuilding it. Most of the material and spare parts he needed to put it together again were old and second hand so a lot of elbow grease was needed to clean them up. Harry proved to be of invaluable help in this respect and spent hours working with him. He would beaver away cleaning wheels, tyres, rods and bits of the engine. I expect doing this work gave him a sense of achievement, a feeling of importance and he became very possessive of his relationship with Tom, even to the extent of warning me and any of my friends to keep away from Tom and the car. It seemed he didn't want us around usurping his position. But at least apart from being a constant bully within the family, Harry managed to keep out of trouble with the law.

Christmas that year came and went, but along the way it seemed to have lost some of its magic. Life was different. Our once tight knit family was beginning to split with my older brothers and sisters going their separate ways. Maggie and Molly were wrapped up in their boyfriends, going to dances and parties and didn't spend much time at home now. Even Daniel seemed to be absent a lot, spending time with new friends he had made at his office. I do recall Maggie and Molly pulling his leg that there must be a girl involved with a rumour circulating – started, I think, by Molly – that he was seeing a young waitress from the cafe he frequented near his office.

For the first time that Christmas there was no stocking for me at the bottom of the bed. It was with sadness and pangs of nostalgia for Christmases past that I watched Walter and Eddie plunder theirs of chocolates, sweets, apples, oranges and even some Brazil nuts.

I did get my own share of the goodies, Mammy saw to that, but the old excitement, the magic of Christmas, was gone.

CHAPTER 16

The great gym shoe robbery

B eing one of the oldest in Swansea, Hafod School was fortunate that it had its own woodworking class. It was one of only a few schools in the area to have one, although they had to share this facility with other schools. It was situated in the basement with two specialist teachers Mr Richards and Mr Aubrey. The school week was divided into 10 separate woodworking sessions – mornings and afternoons – with Hafod School being allocated three of these – Monday, Wednesday and Friday mornings. Other schools were allotted either one or two periods of the remainder.

This was the time along with the other pupils of S2 – Charlie Lewis's class – that I was introduced to the basic skills of woodworking. Both teachers I believe had many years experience of working in the trade as carpenters or shopfitters before taking up their posts as teachers. We benefited greatly from this as both of them treated us as young adults rather than schoolchildren. They were more relaxed and taught by way of demonstration, showing us the correct way to handle the various tools, as these could prove to be very dangerous in the hands of young boys. It was after all a manual skill and perhaps easier to teach than more academic subjects. Each class was divided into two and I was placed with Mr Richards. We sampled the whole spectrum of skills required to make simple objects. These ranged in the first year from a cribbage or bread board, to the final year when we were turning out small items of furniture such as bedside cabinets and meat safes.

One of the first items I made was a parrot cut out of plywood using a fret saw. This was placed on a simple T-shaped stand which we also made and it had a lead weight attached to its tail. With a gentle push the parrot would swing to and fro. These proved to be a great success and were greeted with a mixture of amusement and amazement by our families.

We were taught to use the full range of tools from drawing boards with set squares, jack planes, smoothing planes, hand saws, tenon saws, hammers, chisels and gauges. We were even shown how to mix methylated spirit with shellac to make French polish. One day there was an incident involving the use of meths which provided a salutory lesson for us all when using dangerous materials. Probably because of its volatility it was not kept on the school premises and, whenever this was required, one of the boys had to run down to the local chemist shop to get it. It was dispensed in a large medicine bottle and had to be at the right temperature before it was mixed with the shellac.

In the summer the French polish could be made straight away but in the winter the methylated spirits needed to be slightly warmed. We did this by placing it on top of a radiator which had seemed to work perfectly well in the past. On this particular day either the school boiler was generating extremely hot water or the boys making the

118

French polish left it a little bit too long on the radiator. Anyway, the bottle suddenly exploded with a sound reminiscent of the bombing during the war and everyone, including the teachers, dived under the benches. Fortunately no one was injured but splinters of glass and methylated spirits were sprayed all over the place. This was the first and only time that it happened and Mr Richards took a bit of stick from the headmaster, but no blame was attached to the boys. After that episode I seem to remember that Mr Richards took full responsibility for the methylated spirits whenever it was used.

Another aspect of school life which I thoroughly enjoyed was PT. Each class would have at least one session a week. We would remove our boots and shoes and do physical jerks in our socks. At this time the authorities began to realise that exercise played an important role in the health of the nation – particularly children. To encourage us and make these lessons more attractive, schools were issued with gym shoes. They came in various sizes from very large for the big lads to extremely small for the little ones. There were even some tiny ones for boys like Dinky.

Dinky just loved wearing gym shoes. They were so light on his feet after hobnail boots he said he felt like he was walking on air. Once he had them on it was difficult to get him to take them off. Even after the PT session had finished he would keep running around and bouncing up and down like a rubber ball. So it came as no surprise to me that on one afternoon after school I found him playing in the park still wearing the gym shoes. His last lesson of that day had been PT and he had got so completely carried away with bouncing about that he forgot to change back into his boots before leaving school. Well that's what he said. I think the temptation to keep them on had simply proved too great for him.

"What about your boots mun Dinky?" I asked.

"What you goin' to tell your Mammy."

"I don't know mun," he replied as if he hadn't given any thought to the matter.

"I 'aven't been 'ome yet."

Suddenly I had this horrible thought about his father. Although he had mellowed a lot since first returning from the war, he would still take his belt to Dinky if he was in a foul mood. I was seriously concerned for him. At the risk of ruining Dinky's pleasure at running around in his gym shoes I had to make my point.

"What about your father mun Dinky? He'll cowin' kill you if you 'aven't got your boots."

He hadn't thought about confronting his father until then and for a moment he looked extremely worried. Then he believed he had found a solution to his predicament and his little face brightened up.

"I know Andy" he chirped. "I wont go 'ome until after he's gone down the pub."

But I knew straight away that there was a problem with this and once again I had to remind him.

"You gotta go 'ome for your tea mun. Your mother will come lookin' for you if you don't go 'ome for your tea."

Once more he screwed his face up in deep thought. This time it seemed he didn't have an answer and he looked at me despairingly. This just made me feel guilty because I was the one confronting him with all these problems.

"What am I going to do, Andy mun," he pleaded, "You gotta 'elp me out, right."

This was Dinky all over. I had thought of the problems so I had to come up with the solutions. He had already spent half of his life in my house so there was only one thing for it.

"You'll 'ave to come 'ome with me then. Mammy will give you some bread and jam," I said.

"That's great mun Andy," he said, his face beaming as he started to run off shouting "Come on mun – follow me."

He was off like lightning, for as small as he was, in his gym shoes he was like an Olympic athlete.

I could hardly keep up with him as he tore through the park gates, up the hill and towards – unbelievably I thought – his own house. Dinky boy – you're heading for disaster I thought. But he had already worked out his plan. He knew without doubt that his mother would be in as his father was due home from work and would want his tea straight away. I caught up with him just as he was pushing open the door of his house and shouting down the passageway.

"Mammy! Mammy!"

I could just about hear his mother's muted response from the depths of the kitchen. "Yes, David," she answered.

Against all the odds she still called him David. Whereas everybody else – even his father – called him Dinky.

Quickly he shouted back.

"Mammy. I'm 'aving tea in Andy's 'ouse – right."

We didn't hang about for any arguments on her part, shot off down Odo Street and across the square to my house.

As soon as we went in, Mammy noticed immediately that Dinky was not wearing boots, probably due to the absence of noise on his part as we tore into the kitchen.

"You're quiet Dinky," she said as she looked down at him. "What have you got on then – slippers is it? Oo! There's posh you are."

She took it for granted that he was going to have tea with us as we both sat down at the table, joining Walter and Eddie who were already showing signs that they had nearly finished eating by the tell tale smears of strawberry jam on their faces.

Ten minutes later, with two rounds of bread and jam and a cup of tea in our bellies, we went back outside and headed down to the canal. It was spring 1949 and we had scrounged an empty two pound jam jar from Mammy. The frogs in the canal would be spawning now and we were after some German jelly – frogspawn. We had been collecting frogspawn for years and we knew that if there was any about, the place to get it would be near the bridge by the copperworks.

Surprisingly, after spending an hour or so fruitlessly wading around in the muddy waters, we failed to find any frogspawn. What we did get however was very wet, particularly my boots, but worse still Dinky's 'borrowed' gym shoes. So eventually we decided to call it a day and go home.

We were in a bit of a mess which was not unusual. My boots and socks were wet and I was covered up to my knees in mud, but that didn't unduly worry me. The socks would soon dry out and the boots could be wiped clean. I was still expecting a clout from Mammy though for getting in such a state and once she caught sight of me it was duly delivered. Dinky's school gym shoes were another matter. By the time he got home the mud was beginning to dry out and cake on them. Fortunately his father was still down the pub as he now had no option but to confess to his mother about the gym shoes and enlist her help to clean them up. As expected she gave him a good hiding, but to save him from the wrath of his father she packed him off to bed before scrubbing the gym shoes clean. Then shockingly she did what she thought at the time was a wise thing. They needed to be dried out, but also kept hidden away from his father.

The cooking range in Dinky's kitchen was similar to ours with the oven situated next to an open coal fire. As there was no more cooking to be done that day the fire would soon be damped down for the night. It was then that Dinky's mother had a brainwave – she put them in the oven to dry. Sadly she probably miscalculated the temperature in the oven and the length of time that the gym shoes would be in there. Unfortunately this had a disastrous effect on the gym shoes. When she went to retrieve them the following morning, after Dinky's father had gone to work, she was horrified to see that they had shrunk and were now even smaller than they had been. They were still perfectly formed if a little curled up, but now they would not even fit on Dinky's toes – let alone his feet.

His mother's original plan was that Dinky would wear the gym shoes back to school early that morning but this wouldn't be possible now and was ruled out. Her back-up plan was to get me involved. This brought her banging on our kitchen door at eight o'clock that morning with one of her hands on the scruff of Dinky's neck and the other holding the now distinctly diminutive gym shoes. Although I was completely innocent she was convinced that I was a party to the great gym shoe robbery, so it was up to me to get us out of the mess.

Dinky, looking distinctly guilty, had not argued with his mother, preferring to go along with her thoughts that the two of us were in this mess together. Part of the problem was that Dinky was now wearing just socks as the only pair of boots he possessed were safely locked up in the school.

The main objective, both Mammy and Dinky's mother agreed, was to get Dinky's boots back as quickly as we could. Each of us would have to play a role in this. First, it was up to me to retrieve the boots so that Dinky could attend school where he then would replace the borrowed gym shoes. It wasn't much of a plan I thought and it still left a lot to chance, but off we went with Dinky tip-toeing along in just his socks holding the shrunken gym shoes, one in each hand. I was silently praying that somehow we could retrieve his boots without alerting the teachers. It was still very early, about a quarter past eight, and there were no other boys or teachers about when we went inside the schoolyard. I was hoping that the caretaker was inside preparing the school for the day and that he had left the doors open so I could sneak in and get the boots.

Things went well until, with Dinky pressing me from behind, I slowly turned the door handle and pushed. My heart sank, it was locked. Our great plan had fallen at the first hurdle.

"Come on mun Andy – push harder," he whispered in a really desperate tone.

I knew the situation was hopeless, but to please him I tried the door handle again – giving it a good push. Then disaster struck, or so I thought, when I had heard a voice behind us.

"You can't get in like that Handel – you'll need these," it said.

I spun around almost knocking Dinky to the ground as I did so and there, looming over us, holding a great bunch of keys in his hand, was the tall figure of Mr Richards the woodwork teacher. He stood back eyeing us up and down with a puzzled look on his face. He seemed to be trying to work out what the strange objects in Dinky's hands were. Then it registered with him that the tiny boy standing before him was only wearing socks on his feet.

"Where are your boots my boy?" he asked.

Dinky just stood there, his mouth open and for once in his life he was lost for words. He had decided the best thing to do was to say nothing and let me do the talking.

Mr Richards was a good teacher with an easy going manner, someone the boys looked up to and liked. So I thought I'd come clean with him and blurted out "He left his boots in school yesterday, sir. They're in the gym cupboard in the hall, sir."

I was just about to try to explain what had happened to the gym shoes Dinky was holding in his hands when Mr Richards held his hand up to stop me going any further. He was scrutinising Dinky and the gym shoes, his sharp brain probably working out exactly what had happened to them.

"Don't tell me any more Handel," he said.

"Just take him, get his boots and go home."

He turned the key in the lock, opened the school door and ushered us inside. He didn't mention the gym shoes, but as he left us just said

"Two minutes Handel, that's all and I don't want to see either of you again before nine o'clock."

Two minutes! That was more than enough. We raced up the slope and dashed into the hall. I grabbed the boots while Dinky pushed the shrunken gym shoes as far down to the bottom of the cupboard as he could. Then, holding the boots in one hand and Dinky's arm with the other we raced back down to the yard. The boots were on his feet with the laces tied in a world record time and soon we were back home with his much-relieved mother.

I relived that little escapade on many occasions especially whenever we had a PT lesson. Most of the gym shoes would be in use, but there was always one pair that would remain in the cupboard. They were often looked upon with curiosity, but never again worn.

I often had a feeling that Dinky was occasionally tempted to 'borrow' a pair of the gym shoes again as he took great pleasure in springing about whenever he had them on his feet. Anticipating his intention, I would warn him in advance, that he had been lucky that it was Mr Richards who was at the school door early that morning and not one of the stricter teachers.

If that had been the case his bouncing and springing around would have come about for a far different reason. It would have been down to the pain of the cane on his backside.

CHAPTER 17

Maggie's goal defeats the Swans

When Maggie married Sam early in the summer of 1949, it was every girl's dream come true. She was a June bride with a white wedding. Frantic preparations had been underway for months. The vicar and the church had been booked along with the trestle tables and chairs which were being borrowed from the church hall as the wedding reception was to be in our front room. Maggie and Molly were fitted out with their gowns and Daniel, who was giving Maggie away, had a new suit.

Pride of place at the reception would be given to the wedding cake and this was duly ordered, along with the second most important food item – a whole ox tongue which was going to be boiled and carved by a neighbour who had been a cook on the Great Western Railway's refreshment car service. All this was going to be washed down by a selection of drinks including a barrel of beer arranged by Sid. He was renowned for his judgment of a good pint and knowledge of anything to do with beer and would tap it once the celebrations started.

There was just one snag that could ruin Maggie's big day. The wedding was on a Saturday morning and Swansea Town Football Club – the Swans – were playing at home that afternoon. The kick-off was at three o'clock, the same time that the train taking the happy couple away on their honeymoon would be leaving High Street station. Maggie had apparently threatened Sam that if he attempted to go to the football match then the wedding would be off. Needless to say he was lacking support on this from all quarters. Even his parents were against it. He was their only child and they doted on him, but even they ruled that the match that day was out of bounds. So for the first time in many years, apart from when he was doing his National Service, he missed watching his beloved Swans.

However, as a consolation, Harry who was determined that he was not going to miss out on the match promised that he would give Sam a blow by blow account of the game when he returned. To supplement this he would keep a copy of the Sporting Post which would include a full match report with action pictures. So Sam's fate was sealed. It was a Saturday of mixed blessings as far as he was concerned. It was either Maggie or the football match – and Maggie won.

Everything was in place by the time the big day finally arrived. Mammy was putting the final touches to Maggie and Molly's gowns when the bridegroom's party arrived, minus Sam and his best man of course. They had been sent directly to the church. Sam was not allowed to see Maggie until she was walking down the aisle as it was considered bad luck.

The church was only around the corner so everybody walked there apart from Maggie and Daniel. They travelled in the only transport – the bridal car which would bring Sam and Maggie back after the wedding ceremony. There were no hitches and at eleven o'clock exactly Maggie walked down the aisle with Daniel on her way to become Mrs Sam Bennett.

It seemed to me at the time that the entire population of the Hafod turned out on that bright June day to witness Maggie's wedding. The church was packed and Odo Street was lined with people all waving and cheering as the bridal party passed by. The strong show of support

126

I believed was a tribute to Mammy from the people of the Hafod, for overcoming all the odds and keeping our family together.

Most of the adults managed to squeeze into our front room for the reception while the youngsters gathered in the kitchen. It was no surprise that this included an uninvited guest who didn't want to be left out – Dinky. Mammy had laid on a marvellous spread and everyone agreed that the tongue sandwiches were a treat. Sid tapped the barrel of beer with great enthusiasm, but sadly lost the first couple of pints which sprayed out all over the pantry and bathroom doors before he got on top of the operation. It was fortunate for the adults, but not so for us boys that it was situated in the kitchen for we too got soaked. Sid blamed the landlord of his local for this mishap saying that he had supplied it too fresh. Still, it had a good head on it and all the men agreed that Sid had done a grand job as they set about consuming it.

I clearly remember the scene of devastation on the ground floor of our house when the taxi came to take Sam and Maggie to the station. There were bodies slumped in chairs and on the floor with two of Sam's mates even sprawled outside in the garden. Sid the guardian of the beer barrel which was by now nearly empty had steadfastly remained at his post, only now he too was sat on the floor in a semi-comatose state with Molly nagging him.

"Just look at the state of you mun," she said.

"We're supposed to be going to the station with Maggie and Sam to see them off."

Mammy and Mrs Bennett who seemed to be the only two people who could stand and walk in a straight line were fussing over Maggie and Sam. They warned them to be careful on their journey to their honeymoon with Sam's aunt in Kent as they had to pass through London. Sam, a little bit tipsy himself, was chortling at this.

"Don't you worry Mrs Swain I'll look after Maggie," he said.

"I've been in the Navy – been round the world I 'ave."

Then he bumped his head on the taxi door as the two ladies were pushing him in. Maggie however would not go without Molly seeing her off. "Molly! Molly! Molly!" she shouted. "Come on, we'll miss the train. Leave the daft lello there."

Molly was furious now as she knew that there was no way Sid could make it to the front door, let alone the railway station. She would have to leave him behind, but not without giving him a good kick up the backside. Then, waving her left hand bearing their engagement ring under his nose, she screamed at him.

"You'd better be standing up when I get back or this ring will be going into the fire."

It was at that moment, just before leaving in the taxi that it dawned on Maggie that she wouldn't be returning to us. When the honeymoon was over she was going to live with the Bennetts. I was standing just outside the front door with Walter and Eddie and as she looked at the three of us to wave goodbye, with tears welling up in her eyes, she called us.

"Come here boys," she said putting her arms around the three of us and pulling us close to her. As she kissed each of us on the forehead in turn it was more than a show of affection. It was a demonstration of her great love for us. This was a rare display for Maggie as out of sheer necessity she had always needed to show the world just how strong and determined she was. As she dabbed the tears from her eyes she reverted to the second mother that she had always been to us .

"Now Handel, you look after these two. You must all be good boys for Mammy and when I return in two weeks time you must come straight up and see me."

With that she got into the taxi and Molly squeezed in after her. Then just as Mammy was closing the door she gave us something to look forward to.

"I'm going to make you tea with sandwiches, cakes, jelly and blancmange – and sweets and chocolate too – if I can get them," she shouted above the noise of the taxi engine.

True to her word, when we went to visit her on her return from honeymoon she was waiting for us with a marvellous spread of everything she had promised – including the sweets and chocolate.

Maggie missed us very much and, for many years after that, every Saturday evening we would walk the half mile or so to her home to be stuffed full of goodies to keep us going until the following week.

It was a regular treat we all looked forward to.

CHAPTER 18

Seaside scene caused a stink

Maggie's wedding and consequent leaving home seemed to have stolen the focus of the summer months. There was little to punctuate the holidays which seemed to go on for ever. I went in search of Erica again, to our special place, as I had done several times over the past couple of years. I even climbed up the quarry face and sprang from the ledge at the top to the overhanging tree, but I hadn't seen her since the time when I first discovered her hideout. I kept my promise not to reveal the place, not even to Dinky, but that seemed to be futile now as a secret is not worth having if it's not shared with someone special. I kept hoping that one day she would return and we would recapture some of the magic we had experienced on that special day. I wondered whether she ever came home from the young ladies college in Cheltenham or if as a young lady now she had put her childhood dreams and pleasures aside.

At the start of the autumn term in September 1949 I moved into Mr Thomas's class – S3. Titus Thomas was the school's music teacher, a gruff, rotund man, a former rugby player who had no time for mamby-pambies or cry babies. One word would sum up just what he expected of the boys in his class – endeavour. For most of us this would be our last full year of school. When you reached the age of 15 your schooldays were over. Mr Thomas was a clever teacher. He quickly assessed the strengths and weaknesses of the boys in his class and split us into groups according to our ability. For some it was their last chance to ensure they had a working knowledge of the three Rs as each boy was pushed to his limit.

Titus Thomas was also aware that a number of us were not being stretched by the standard of arithmetic being taught and he had procured some books, published by a company called Larcombe, for ten of us. These included subjects like geometry and logarithms which made the subject more interesting. As a result we became known as the Larcombe Boys.

Due to the change in the school year, Tommy Thomas previously in the year above me was now in my class. He had an uncle who was a trawlerman and was spending more time down at the docks helping out on the boat. This was a good move for Tommy as he had ambitions of becoming a trawlerman himself. He developed a keen interest in all things connected to the sea, marine life in particular, so I greeted with some enthusiasm an idea that he put to me. On reflection perhaps I should have thought a little more about it.

His suggestion concerned an aquarium that Mr Thomas kept in the classroom for the study of pond and river life. Tommy believed that the meagre fresh water flora and fauna on display in the fish tank could be greatly improved upon. He felt the tank should hold a seawater display and better reflect our area as a coastal town.

"Hey 'andel, mun," he said.

"Do you think Mr Thomas would like a change with that fish tank. We could make it into a lovely sea water fish tank with shrimps and cockles and periwinkles and bits of different seaweed."

Brilliant ideas were not usually associated with Tommy and I was

surprised by this rather innovative proposition. I was also a little envious that he had thought of it rather than me.

"Aye mun Tommy," I replied, only too happy to be linked with what I though was a winning idea.

"We can put sand and rocks in the bottom and see if we can get some little fish too."

My contribution to the plan added some final touches which I thought would make it even better. I felt extremely proud and agreed to put the scheme to Mr Thomas. Looking back now I don't believe he was quite switched on that day, or perhaps he had some more important thoughts on his mind, as he agreed without question. So after dinner the following Friday, with Mr Thomas's permission, we set off for Swansea Beach lugging a small milk churn into which we would put our finds for the new aquarium.

Tommy's uncle, who must have been ever so proud of him, was to meet up with us at the beach to lend a hand. We knew exactly where we could get all that we needed. Half way between the west pier and the Slip there was a small area covered with rocks and stones where we could collect the sand, seawater, seaweed, small rocks and stones and some periwinkles. Tommy's uncle had promised some shrimps, cockles and small fish which he duly delivered.

It was a bit of a struggle lugging the milk churn, now half full with our finds on the beach, back to school, but with a sense of triumph we arrived back there just when the rest of the pupils were leaving. It was Friday – the best day of the week with no more school until Monday. Even the teachers were in a hurry to get away.

Mr Thomas told us to complete the new sea aquarium and the caretaker would let us out when we had finished. The fish tank had already been cleaned of its old fresh water life so it wasn't long before we had filled it with the contents of the milk churn.

At first it looked a bit of a mess but once the cloudiness of the water cleared it looked grand. The little sea creatures looked at home among the rocks and seaweed of various shapes and colours. We felt it was a job well done and one that would earn us praise. For once we could barely wait for Monday morning to come and for Mr Thomas and the rest of the class to see it. Monday was the busiest day of the week for Mammy, getting everyone back to school or work and replenishing the food stock after the weekend. There were always plenty of errands to run so normally I would be dashing to school through empty streets just making it in time for assembly. Today was no different except that when I arrived there, crowds of parents and children were gathered around the school gates. I wondered what was wrong and was preventing them from entering the school? I soon found out. As I approached the crowd milling around the school gates someone broke away and ran towards me – it was my best pal Dinky.

"Hey, Andy boy – your in for it mun," he whispered with a look of horror on his face as he walked alongside me. I quickened my pace as he elaborated on his news.

"The 'eadmaster wants to see you quick mun. Everybody says it's your fault that we can't go into school."

I hurried through the school gates as the people gathered there stood back and opened a path for me. I could sense hundreds of eyes watching me and there were looks of scorn and disapproval on the faces of some of the parents. When I reached the schoolyard I was greeted by about four hundred boys yelling and screaming at me. Some were even cheering and clapping their hands.

"It's better than the pong works 'andel," I heard one shout above the tremendous din.

I was baffled. I couldn't understand what all the fuss and commotion was about – and how I was involved. I didn't have to wait long for the answer however. The voice of Mr Joe Morgan the headmaster bellowed across the yard immediately quelling the noise from the children.

"You – Handel Swain – come here boy – quickly now."

He was standing by the main entrance with Mr Thomas who I observed was not looking his usual, robust, authoritative self.

I got the first whiff, the initial hint of odour, as I neared the two men and my sense of smell didn't need to be at its peak as I got closer.

"Can you smell that, boy?" bellowed Joe Morgan, pointing to the open doors of the school's main entrance.

"Inside now Handel and help Tommy Thomas to clean out that cesspit of an aquarium that you've inflicted on us."

It was only then that I noticed every door and window in the entire building was open as wide as possible. The contents of our proud new sea aquarium had the entire warm September weekend to simmer and as a result had created the most obnoxious stew. The stench from the decaying seaweed and the dead or dying creatures had even spread to the girls and infants schools. I raced through the door and up to the classroom only to be confronted by the most vile stench I have ever experienced. It was only the presence of Mr Morgan blocking my way of escape that gave me the courage to keep on going to find Tommy and the source of the problem. Mercifully, by the time I arrived he had almost completed cleaning out the fish tank using an old tin mug and a couple of fire buckets.

"Oh I feel sick mun 'andel," he moaned, his face haggard and pale.

I knew what he meant. The contents of the tank that only a couple of days before had carried the fresh aroma of the sea were now giving off a rotten, nausea-inducing smell.

I didn't really want to say anything. That would mean having to open my mouth whereas all I wanted to do was hold my breath. Through pursed lips I could only mutter "Mm – Mm – Mm," as I picked up one of the buckets and headed for the door. It was only then that I spoke and asked what might seem an obvious question.

"What are we goin' to do with this stuff now, Tommy?" I said.

"We gotta take it to the lavs mun and flush it down. That's what Mr Morgan told me."

The thought of carrying the buckets with their putrid contents filled me with horror. It would mean having to cross the entire width of the schoolyard, running the gauntlet of four hundred jeering voices, but face them we had to as there was no alternative route. Carrying a bucket each we walked down the slope and entered the arena. Of course Tommy, being a big strong lad, carrying a bucket which was over three quarters full was easy. He virtually sprinted across the yard and disappeared into the lavatory before the boys had really wound themselves up, but I found it hard going. I hadn't got half way across that yard before I tired.

With my knees beginning to wobble and the liquid slime sloshing about to a chorus of yelling and shouting I stopped and put the bucket down. It was then that the first whistle blew saving me from any further humiliation – Mr Thomas had come to my rescue. The school ruling was that on the sound of the first whistle all boys would immediately stop, stand still and remain silent. The response was instant, for failure to obey would result in at least one stroke of the cane. So at least I was spared any further cries of derision as Mr

Thomas called out: "Not you Handel. You carry on going and be quick about it."

That brief respite was all that I needed. Using both hands I picked up the bucket and dragged it and myself to the lavatory. The second whistle sounded then which was the signal for the boys to form lines ready to enter the school.

For several weeks afterwards Tommy and I were inevitably greeted by boys holding their noses and calling us names like smelly stinker or pong works, but there were no hard feelings or blame held against us by the headmaster or by Mr Thomas.

He probably realised that a marine aquarium in the classroom was not a good idea. The sea is never still, its waters constantly cleansed by the movement of the tides and although the experiment resulted in disaster, we learned that nothing is achieved without endeavour.

CHAPTER 19

Mrs Smeller the fortune teller

The departure of Maggie left a huge void in the Swain household. She was such a dominant character within the family that it took a long time to get accustomed to the loss. We had to adjust to life without her, with perhaps Mammy suffering the most as she had come to depend on her eldest child for so much.

I didn't realise it then, although probably Mammy did, that Maggie was virtually irreplaceable. Almost single-handedly she helped to bring some order to our family, allowing Mammy to concentrate on the basics of life such as keeping us sheltered, fed and clothed. Fortunately however, she was not too far away and visited frequently which did help to ease the situation. As well as our weekly visits to her new home every Saturday evening, she would also call with her husband Sam to collect Harry on their way to the Vetch Field to see the Swans whenever they played at home.

As always, whenever there is a void created in life, something or someone will come along to fill it. For us that someone was a funny, but extremely odd old lady that we knew as Mrs Smeller – fortune teller. Her real name was Mrs Mellor but said quickly it sounded like Mrs Smeller. We thought that was a much more fitting sounding name for a cranky old lady who predicted the future by reading tea leaves. She was almost witch-like in appearance – tall and skinny with a huge hook of a nose and lank, grey shoulder-length hair always partly

covered with a headscarf. She wore a long tweed overcoat that reached down to her ankles and was always buttoned up – summer or winter. With men's black shoes on her large feet, she walked with an awkward, jerky gait and plodded along like a circus clown.

Mammy always kept Mrs Mellor at a distance when she sat at the kitchen table as she had loose dentures and a tendency to spray her unsuspecting host with half the tea she had just drunk. This odd woman's strange family included a husband and a daughter called Millie. Mammy had always been a little superstitious. Even before she met Mrs Mellor she would always try to avoid the obvious harbingers of bad luck such as walking under ladders and breaking mirrors. After meeting this crackpot of a woman however, Mammy's list of things that might awaken the spirits of doom seemed to grow and grow.

A new 'do or do not' would be added after each of the fortune teller's visits. The growing list included no more whistling in the house, no cutting of nails on Fridays or Sundays, if a right hand glove fell to the floor it had to be picked up by the left hand and vice versa and countless others. The most comical of these, as far as we were concerned, was that visitors to the house had to leave by the door through which they had entered. In our case, apart from Maggie's wedding, this was always at the back door because we never used the front one. Although we greeted these new superstitions with scepticism we had to go along with Mammy and carry out the rituals involved because she took them so seriously.

Mrs Mellor's forte, or black art we thought and for which she was renowned locally, was her skill at reading tea leaves. This service was one that she rendered purely for pleasure and never charged for, though there was always the consolation of at least two cups of tea plus the odd Welsh cake or biscuit. She could see all manner of images in the tea leaves left at the bottom of a cup. There were ships coming in or pots of gold which indicated money might be on its way; a long winding road suggesting someone was going on a journey and tall dark strangers – to be wary of. Mostly the clever Mrs Mellor only saw signs that would bring good luck, so as long as Mammy was on her guard against tall dark strangers everything would be fine.

Mrs Mellor's visits to our house were by invitation only so although the rest of us, especially Maggie and Molly, thought she was an absolute fraud, she was not an unwelcome guest. When Mammy felt a bit down, or needed reassuring that life would turn out for the better, she would ask one of us, usually me, to nip down to the Mellor's house just a five minute walk away and invite her up.

It was during one of these visits that I met Mr Mellor. He was a short, plump man with a bald head and bright rosy cheeks who always sat in an old wooden armchair. In the summer he would sit just outside the front door and in the winter just inside, in the passageway. He smoked a pipe but seemed to spend most of his time picking away with his thumbnail at a roll of 'twist' tobacco. Mrs Mellor told Mammy that she had to watch him with his pipe, particularly if he ran short of tobacco, as he had no qualms about raiding the tea caddy.

"He'll smoke the dry tea leaves, Mrs Swain," she complained.

"It's disgusting. Smoking the twist tobacco is bad enough, but dry tea leaves – it's a foul habit."

It was probably his love of smoking that kept him banished to the passageway and outside of the house. The fresh air obviously did him some good as his cheeks were rosy and glowing in stark contrast to his wife and daughter who both displayed pallid complexions. Their daughter Millie was a timid girl who could not have been given a more inappropriate name – Millie Mellor. She looked a lot older than her age which was probably about thirty five. Like her mother she was tall and skinny with scrawny features. She did however lack the splendour of her mother's hook nose.

Millie usually wore a belted man's raincoat that was much too big for her and always buttoned up. Her long hair was mousy, unkempt and of uneven length. She either trimmed it herself or her mother cut it for her. The closest Millie came to showing a hint of femininity, although she never quite managed to acquire the skill in wearing them, was when she donned high heeled shoes. It was a sight to behold. When she managed to escape the sanctuary of her house she would walk in the middle of road, her high heels scraping the tarmac and her face filled with anguish. She would be constantly glancing back over her shoulder, though exactly why was beyond my comprehension. I put it down to the fact that the whole family were odd and eccentric.

When Mrs Mellor first began visiting us Mammy would shoo us out of the house, but as we got to know the family better, particularly Mrs Mellor, she would allow us to stay as long as we remained quiet. So at long last we got to witness at first hand the ritual of reading the tea leaves. Usually just Walter, Eddie and me, but sometimes Molly would join in. Mammy was always well prepared for Mrs Mellor's visit. She would have the teapot, cups and a plate of Welsh cakes or biscuits ready, but before the tea was poured it was essential that Mrs Mellor tapped the teapot lid three times. Only then would Mammy proceed to fill the cups. The pot would be shaken around to get the brew inside swirling around and ensure that it had a good volume of leaves mixed in. Then both ladies would settle down and have a chat whilst drinking the tea with Mrs Mellor doing most of the talking, keeping Mammy up to date with the local gossip. She always seemed to get in a bit about her husband, complaining about his pipe and how lazy he was.

One day Mrs Mellor told us how she and her daughter Millie had once played a trick on him. Apparently whenever her husband had finished his stint in the passageway or outside the house, he would drag his old chair to the kitchen table and plant himself down in front of the fire. This is where he sat at meal times and in the evenings to listen to the wireless. On this particular day Mrs Mellor had opened a tin of pilchards in tomato sauce which they were going have with some bread and butter for their tea. But unfortunately by the time his wife had set the table and dished out the pilchards, Mr Mellor, aided by the heat of the fire had fallen asleep. It seems this was not an unusual event as he had a habit of nodding off for a few minutes but would soon be woken by the sound of cutlery clinking on plates. On this occasion however, he continued with his nap.

Mrs Mellor and Millie had finished their tea but the head of the household was still in a deep sleep. They both sat there wondering. When he'd wake up? Would he wake up? Would he want the pilchards? Did he really need them? Eventually the temptation became too great. They had convinced themselves that he was not going to wake up and the pilchards would only go to waste. So Mrs Mellor swapped her empty plate for her husband's and divided the fish between herself and Millie. She was convinced that Mr Mellor would never be any the wiser when he finally woke, but would just think that he had enjoyed a fine tea of bread and butter and pilchards before dropping off to sleep. After all, the evidence – the empty plate – would be in front of him. Just to add a final touch she carefully smeared a little tomato sauce around his lips.

It was easy to imagine the scene when he finally did wake up, of him being a little confused and bewildered looking down at the dirty plate and smacking his lips. It proved to us that Mrs Mellor was not without a sense of humour.

After the initial chit chat, when both ladies had drunk their tea, it was time to get down to the serious business of reading the tea leaves. Mrs Mellor would sit up straight and there'd be complete silence.

"Are you ready Mrs Swain?" she would ask.

Mammy would remain silent just nodding her head that she was indeed ready then Mrs Mellor would carefully lift the cup and peer down into its murky dregs. This was where the fortune teller's special art came in. She would gently swirl the cup, tipping it this way then that way before disposing of the remaining liquid to cast a pattern of leaves around the sides and bottom of the cup. Then, almost in a trance, she would gaze at the leaves and concentrate her formidable mind on deciphering the shapes and forms they revealed.

There was always an agonising wait before Mrs Mellor finally discovered a familiar shape or form emerging from a cluster of the tea leaves. Then, in a soft whisper, she would tell us to 'hush', fearing that in our excitement we would react by talking or become boisterous which would disturb the forces revealing the mysterious shapes of the tea leaves.

Slowly and deliberately she would give Mammy her interpretation of the patterns on display. Deciphering the codes in the tea leaves she would generally suggest that they revealed that things were taking a turn for the best, that Lady Luck was smiling down on the Swain family or things were looking up and good fortune was coming.

Mammy always seemed to gain great comfort from the fact that good fortune was just around the corner. Whether that good fortune did ever arrive on our doorstep was, of course, another matter.

CHAPTER 20

Purr-fect way to replace old Puss

All too soon another member of our family was leaving home. Daniel was 18 and November 1949 brought his departure for National Service. Daniel was joining the Royal Army Pay Corps. He had chosen this branch of the services as it enabled him to continue with the same job as he had in civvy street, that of a clerk book-keeper.

Although she was sad to see him leave Mammy was glad that he had avoided joining a front line regiment. The Second World War had been over for four years, but the world was still a dangerous place especially for soldiers. There was tension in Europe, the Middle and Far East, all places where our servicemen were actively involved. Mammy believed that Daniel was too quiet and reserved for the tough life of an infantryman. She felt it was far better for him to be in an office. So off he went one dreary November day, destined for far-flung Salisbury Plain and Devizes, where he would do his basic training for six weeks. It was an area of the country completely unknown to us. He was catching the 9.30am train from High Street station to Cardiff which was a step into the unknown in itself. There, he would change for Bristol where he would finally change again for Devizes. It seemed to be a journey full of hidden dangers and might as well have been to the far side of the moon for a traveller of such little experience as Daniel. His greatest adventure until then had been a Sunday school outing to Porthcawl. Mammy made him promise that he would write a letter and post it home to us that very same day. Sure enough the letter was delivered by first post the following morning confirming that he had arrived at his Army barracks safe and well.

The steady but inexorable break-up of our family had begun with Maggie getting married and then Daniel going off to the Army. Mammy believed such things like bad luck, always went in threes. Perhaps she was right, for shortly before Christmas we lost the third member of our family – Puss the cat.

Puss had been with us for eight years although she had never changed from the scrawny animal that always seemed to treat us with disdain. She was the cause of a great deal of annoyance to both ourselves and our neighbours, particularly at night when she was in season, as the tom cats would seek her out with their wailing cries of love. Then of course there was the inevitable birth of her offspring which Mammy would need to dispose of in her own quiet way.

We didn't notice Puss's absence for a few days. It was just before Christmas and extra arrangements were being made as Daniel was expected home from the Army for a few days. Anyway it was not unusual for her to go walkabout for a few days. But when she had not returned after about a week, Mammy, fearing the worst, insisted that we scoured the area for her. It was strange that Mammy who seemed to be forever cursing and scolding Puss was now bemoaning her loss. The old cat was like a selfish and cantankerous relative who had come to lodge with us, taking everything but offering nothing and believing her very presence was gratitude enough. Even so, Puss had filled a

gap in our lives, coming as she had after the death of my father and the bombing of our home. Now Puss was gone and we missed her. She had always looked old and scraggy so we didn't know her real age. Mammy believed that cats, when they were preparing to die, would find a secluded place and go into a deep sleep from which they would never wake. I wondered whether they were like elephants. I had read that these massive and intelligent creatures had a secret graveyard where they would go to die, a holy place that mankind would never discover. I felt better when I thought of this believing that Puss too, was now at peace resting in the mysterious distant hills.

Mammy took the opportunity of Puss's disappearance to lay down a new rule – no more cats! That decree lasted less than a week. Dinky, who spent more time in our house than his own, decided that Mammy's rule didn't apply to him. He missed Puss and believed the house wasn't the same without her so he decided to get a cat – but it would live with us.

When he told me this I refused to take any notice, believing that he was in no position to get a cat. I was horrified when, within days of Mammy's new rule, he appeared on our doorstep carrying a cute little bundle of black and white fur – a kitten which he had christened Penny. I reserved judgment on this, but Walter and Eddie were delighted. They didn't mind Puss, but they didn't particularly like her either because of her no-nonsense attitude to life. She was prone to hissing and spitting or swiping at them with her claws so they had wisely learned to keep their distance.

There were no such reservations about this little kitten as it sat pert and bright in Dinky's arms, soaking up all the fuss and attention being showered on her. Mammy was having none of this though. Puss had been her cat. She had encouraged it to stay and suffered the consequences. The cat was her responsibility and she accepted that, but she was not going to have another foisted upon her by Dinky, Walter, Eddie or anyone else. She stood up and with an accusing glare at me she scolded the four of us. And out came the Welsh.

"Na! Na! bach – No! No! boy," she said, wagging her finger.

"That kitten is not staying in this house."

Dinky had an immediate ally in Walter.

"Oh, Mammy, it's lovely mun why can't we 'ave it?" he pleaded.

"Because I said no more cats didn't I," she replied swiftly. "And another reason is because it's a girl cat and she will have kittens."

Dinky was prepared for this and in a flash enlightened Mammy.

"Girl cats can't 'ave kittens Mrs Swain they're too young see."

But Mammy wasn't falling for this either and with an exaggerated shaking of her head and almost laughing at his cheek answered him.

"Yes Dinky boy, but girl cats grow up to be lady cats see and lady cats have kittens." There was a slight pause before she added "And that's the main reason we're not having another cat!"

Dinky stared down at the floor, a beaten man. Mammy's words were forceful and final. He had given the argument for keeping the kitten his best shot, but had failed. It was pointless for me to say anything. I knew only too well the reason why she was so adamant. A silence followed during which Walter, with a pitiful look in his eyes, continued stroking the kitten. We were all waiting for Mammy to tell Dinky that he must take it back where he had it from. I was waiting for the floodgates to open with Walter as I could see the tears welling up in his eyes. Thankfully for us all the kitchen door was pushed open and in came Sid in his bus conductor's uniform. He sensed the cold atmosphere filling the kitchen right away – Mammy, stone-faced confronting Dinky, Walter, and Eddie with me in a state of silent neutrality.

"Aye, Aye. Who's been murdered in by 'ere then?" he chirped, with his hands on his hips and a big grin on his face.

Although he was not yet married to Molly, Sid had made himself very much at home in our family – he was like a big brother now. He even called Mammy, Mam and he had a way of getting around her. He knew everything – or thought he did. Sid was the eternal optimist and believed that there was always a solution to every problem.

"Oo! What have you got by there Dinky boy?" he asked as he leaned down and gently took the kitten from Dinky's arms. Then raising it to his face he began talking to it like he would to a baby.

"Whose a lovely boy then? You're gorgeous aren't you. I'm your Uncle Sid, I am," he coo'd. Mammy was aware of Sid's charm and decided to get in first before he could start working on her.

"That's the trouble Sid. It's not a boy. It's a girl. You know what she'll be having in a few months and I'm not putting up with it."

Her little speech didn't deter Sid one bit.

144

"Oh, but she's lovely Mam. Just look at her, she's gorgeous mun."

Then he played an unexpected trump card. "Don't you worry about kittens Mam. These days we can 'ave 'er doctored," he said with an enthusiasm that was rubbing off on everyone including me and I couldn't resist adding my voice to the argument pleading "Yes Mammy take 'er to the doctor mun."

And although like me they didn't have a clue what it meant about the kitten being 'doctored' Dinky, Eddie and Walter joined in chanting Doctor! Doctor! Doctor!

Mammy was beginning to soften, the stern edge to her voice weakened as she tried to resist this onslaught against her will.

"What about the cost Sid? It's out of the question. I can't afford it mun."

If it's a question of money, I thought, that could be our downfall. Mammy had no spare cash for spending on kittens. But our hopes were revived when Sid announced "There's no need for money Mam," as slowly and deliberately he continued "The PDSA will do it for nothing."

Mammy didn't have a response, she was defeated. She sat down in her chair raised her arms and nodded her head in a gesture that she was giving in, resigned to the fact that the kitten was staying. True to his word Sid arranged everything and eventually Penny the kitten was transported in a cardboard box to the PDSA surgery. She had generated a lot of excitement and everyone agreed that Sid was a good person to have on your side. We believed that he knew everything – well certainly about cats and kittens anyway.

Dinky and I embarked on a great debate as to just what the doctor was going to do to prevent Penny from having kittens. There was a lot of speculation and a bit of confusion too as Sid said the person doing the operation was an animal doctor called a vet. But all this ended when Harry who did not care whether we had a kitten or not brought the debate to an end with some finality.

"You kids don't know anything about cats being doctored mun," he said, before sending us into a state of total confusion.

"They're going to cut her cock off, mun."

That can't be right I thought.

"But it's a girl cat mun. They 'aven't got cocks like us," I said.

"Of course they 'ave mun, 'ow do you think they 'ave a pee then," he said. "Because it's 'idden inside 'em right?"

I thought what he was saying was preposterous but I knew better than to continue arguing with him. Trying to prove him wrong would only annoy him with the probable result that I would get a punch to my kidneys or a slap around the head. I decided to wait until Sid came back with the kitten. He would have the answer I was sure. All of this was forgotten though when Sid, accompanied by Molly, who was holding Penny, eventually arrived home that night. We were all eagerly waiting their return. Walter, Eddie, Dinky and me and even Mammy seemed pleased when they turned up with the kitten which was looking fine. But they had some startling news. Whoever had told Dinky that Penny was a girl cat was wrong. It was in fact a boy.

"So Dinky boy, your Penny has turned out to be a Bob," said Sid.

The vet had confirmed that the kitten Dinky christened Penny was in fact a tom cat which no doubt pleased Mammy as she was doubly sure now that there would be no further kittens to dispose of. Mammy, Sid and Molly thought that it was hilarious. They laughed at Sid's words to Dinky and agreed that the kitten should now be rechristened Bob. But Dinky was having none of this and neither were Walter and Eddie. They didn't care whether it was a he cat or a she cat, to them its name was going to remain Penny. Mam, Sid, Molly and even I tried to persuade them that Bob would be a better name.

"His name is Bob mun Dinky," I argued.

"You can't have a boy cat with a girl's name."

But he was adamant that the kitten's name would be Penny. And he was in an extremely strong position. He had Walter and Eddie backing him as he retorted "Well 'e don't look like a Bob to me. He looks more like a Penny."

Then with a look of triumph on his face he turned to my younger brothers and said "What are you going to call it 'en boys?"

They answered in unison, almost singing the name and kept repeating 'Penny! Penny! Penny! Penny!'

For a while the adults continued to insist on calling the kitten Bob, but they were fighting a losing battle. I caved in immediately as I was sure that it would only respond to whichever name Walter and Eddie called it and that was going to be Penny.

Within a year it had matured into a superb specimen. A gorgeous black and white tom cat which remained frisky and kittenish for most of its life. We could play, stroke, cuddle and even tease him without the hint of a hiss or a scratch from a claw unlike his mean and scrawny predecessor, Puss. He was indeed a loving and friendly cat especially with children. There was one exception however, a little girl that he was extremely wary of – Dinky's young sister, Gladdie. As soon as she was able to walk Gladdie became like Dinky's shadow, following him everywhere. Like most children she had boundaries imposed on her, but from an early age she was allowed to follow Dinky the short distance from their home in Odo Street to our house.

Like Dinky and the rest of her family Gladdie was tiny. She was a petite blonde-haired girl with large, inquisitive, blue eyes that seemed too big for her head. She was boisterous, bossy and fussy, constantly babbling on in a language that seemed alien to us. Probably copying a lot of these traits from her brother she would descend upon us like a whirlwind. Immediately she entered our house she caused disruption by getting under everyone's feet or bouncing on the couch. She would open cupboards and drawers and most painful, at least for the cat, persist in trying to grab it by its tail. It soon learned however that there was an escape route from this yelling banshee of a baby.

As soon as there was any indication Gladdie was on her way, Penny would take refuge under the couch. You wouldn't believe a mouse could squeeze under there let alone Penny, but that is just what he did and there he stayed until the coast was clear again. We loved to see Gladdie coming as we would be in stitches at her antics, but after five minutes in her presence we would be exhausted and plead with Dinky to take her home.

Penny was a welcome addition to the family and would be a pleasant surprise for Daniel who was due home for his first spell of leave on the night before Christmas Eve. His train was due into High Street at 8.15pm and Mammy and Maggie went to greet him. It was dark when they arrived home but that wasn't a problem any more. Unlike the early days of the war we had electric light in every room of the house now. And what a surprise we had when eventually they returned home with Daniel for they came by taxi. It was almost unheard of. Nobody in the Hafod used taxis unless it was for weddings and funerals. Perhaps it was the sight of my brother in his smart uniform with belt and gaiters all brassy and shiny and his gleaming black boots, but he must have looked too good to come by bus, so between them Mammy and Maggie paid for the taxi.

Christmas started early that year. It was the first party I believe we ever had. Mammy had prepared sandwiches and Welsh cakes, Sam and Maggie brought sweets, chocolates and pop for us children while Sid, who was soon to marry Molly, came with beer for the grown-ups and a special bottle of Mackeson stout for Mammy. It was the first time since Maggie's wedding that all the family were together again. I cannot remember what time I went to bed that night. It was very late, I know and it was a good job too, that there was no school the following day. Even Mammy had a lie-in, which was most unusual as she normally got up at six o'clock every morning to set the fire and prepare breakfast.

Christmas day came with the usual chicken dinner and Christmas pudding. I was glad Daniel was home with us once more – if not for long, but sad that Maggie was missing from the table. She did come for tea, but stayed only briefly as she and her husband Sam along with Molly and Sid went off with their friends. They even took Daniel, eager to show him off in his spanking new Army uniform.

The high hopes that I had harboured for a wonderful Christmas with the family together, had it seemed evaporated and an air of sadness descended on me, bringing with it the realisation that my life was changing once again.

CHAPTER 21

Saying farewell
to childhood

I can't remember much about the remainder of Christmas 1949 except for the fact that it probably marked the end of my childhood days. That was the time when I realised that Mammy had become Mam. Maggie and Molly called her Mammy for as long she lived. I suppose it is something that girls can get away with, but boys become men and the word Mammy was not for them. Unwittingly at first, I followed the path of tradition and copied Daniel and Harry – Mammy was now Mam. It was part of the growing-up process I was now experiencing. My voice was changing and sometimes I seemed to lose control of my larynx which without warning would suddenly plummet from alto to bass. There were other hormonal changes too. I was becoming preoccupied with girls. Dreaming of them by day – and certainly by night. It was the spring of 1950 and I was 14.

In June of that year the world was thrown into turmoil once more with a new war in the far east. Conflict broke out in Korea when the Communist north, backed by China, attacked the Democratic south. As a result a United Nations force led by the Americans and including a large British contingent went to the aid of South Korea. It was another war in a far-off country of which we had little knowledge. For most people it was baffling as to why we were involved as there was no apparent direct threat to us as a country. Of course now that we had entered the war there was a direct threat to our family as Daniel was still in the Army. Many National Servicemen fought in the Korean War and a lot of lives were lost, but thankfully Daniel was spared. One consequence of the war was that National Service was extended from eighteen months to two years so he had to serve an extra six months. After initial heavy fighting the war developed into one of attrition with peace finally being restored in July 1953.

Despite this far-away conflict, life in the Hafod went on very much as before. I was still captain of the green team and my vice-captain now was Simon Veal, an odd, nervy boy, a bit of a loner who hardly ever spoke. Making vice captain at least proved that he wasn't dull. He was extremely erratic and his schoolwork suffered accordingly. Sometimes he did very well but at other times performed poorly. His one redeeming feature though was his excellent singing voice.

On special occasions such as Christmas or St David's Day, Simon would give solo performances of his favourite song 'Where ere you walk' in front of the whole school. Apparently his mother had decided that by singing he would gain in confidence and she paid for him to have private lessons. She was probably right in this as he certainly showed no fear when exercising his vocal chords.

It was not for his prowess at singing that I remember Simon however. He had an unpleasant and annoying habit of playing with his private parts. This was not just a case of what we called pocket billiards either. Instead he would openly display his manhood, cradling it in the palm of his hands and sometimes – disgustingly – stretching the thing. Simon would often become distracted and start playing with himself when we were at our desks listening to a wireless programme or a talk by Mr Thomas.

Whether any of the others noticed this lad's odd habit I don't know, but I was unfortunate enough to be sitting next to him and eventually it began to get on my nerves. After a few weeks I reached breaking point. It came while we were listening to John Bunyan's Pilgrims Progress on BBC schools' radio. The classroom resonated with the shouting and baying of the crowd in the story which had really captured the imagination of the class. Except that is for Simon who, hands hidden below the lid of the desk, was stroking his manhood again. I had my wooden rule in my hand and suddenly the temptation to put an end to his activities became irresistible and I gave him a sharp rap right on his privates. The note Simon's voice let out that day was undoubtedly the highest and sharpest he had ever hit in his life. The sudden yelp focussed every pair of eyes in the classroom on us. I simply continued to stare straight ahead and pretended that I had not seen or heard anything and in any case it had nothing to do with me. Puzzled looks were exchanged around the classroom as Simon continued bawling, but quickly and wisely he tried to camouflage this with a fit of coughing. He now had one hand covering his mouth with the other tightly clutching his now sore private parts.

Simon continued coughing and spluttering until Mr Thomas became fed up with him.

"That boy – Simon Veal," he yelled. "Be quiet. You're spoiling the play. If you've got something stuck in your throat go down to the cloakroom and get a drink of water."

Simon was out of his seat and bolting through the door almost before the words had left the teacher's mouth. The sight of Simon scurrying out of the classroom brought howls of laughter from the rest of the boys. Mr Thomas just shook his head in disbelief. With Simon out of the way Mr Thomas quickly restored order and soon we were caught up once more in the exploits of Christian and the Pilgrim's Progress. Nobody ever discovered what had happened that day. Neither Simon nor I, ever mentioned the episode. I think we both felt a little ashamed. Thankfully it did put an end to his preoccupation with his privates – in the classroom at least. Little did I know then but before very long I would suffer my own spot of embarrassment.

On the first day back in school after the Whitsun holiday it was announced that the swimming baths at Morriston had reopened. Those who wanted to attend the baths were told to bring a towel and bathing trunks to school the following Friday. There was great excitement among the boys as many had heard of the high diving boards there, including a sprung board.

All this talk of diving boards however didn't mean much to me as I had never before been anywhere near a swimming baths. Until now I had only paddled in Llewellyn Park pond and the sea off Swansea Beach. I had no idea how to swim. Still everyone was clamouring to go and I was no exception. I was determined to be on the bus to the baths on Friday. But before then there was one small problem to overcome. I had to get hold of some swimming trunks. All of my previous encounters with the sport of bathing had been carried out in the 'nacker' as we called being nude. Having such things as swimming trunks I knew was a luxury that Mam couldn't afford, but I was not going to be deterred by that – I was going to make some.

During and just after the war we had received, through the Salvation Army, many clothes parcels from America. These consisted mainly of children's garments. In one there was a roll of sturdy flannelette out of which Mam, who wasn't very good with a needle and thread had done her best to make us some underwear and pyjamas. She kept this material in an old metal trunk in the box room and I knew there was enough left to make some swimming trunks.

I had a rough idea of what they looked like and I devised a plan. I cut out two pieces of the cloth shaped like a wide letter Y, sewed them together and hey presto I had a pair of swimming trunks. I thought they looked quite good – just like the real thing. Unfortunately instead of just sitting back and admiring my handiwork I should have tried them on. If I had done then I might have been saved a lot of embarrassment later.

Friday came and with it the bus to the swimming baths. They were a revelation. Fortunately the weather was bright and sunny for all it consisted of was a plain rectangular pool about twenty yards by ten lined with sky blue tiles. To my surprise it was in the open air. At first I thought that the pool looked ever so inviting and like the rest of the boys I just couldn't wait to get into the water. We piled into the

changing rooms where I now discovered most of the boys were already wearing their swimming trunks under their clothes. In no time at all they had stripped off and were rushing back outside where I could hear them whooping and yelling, jumping and diving into the pool. So having to change into my brand new bathers I was the last boy out. Still I was rather pleased with my handiwork and I thought they fitted alright – if a little slack around my bottom.

This swimming lark was all new to me, but I too rushed outside getting caught up in the boisterous excitement of the boys milling about in the water. Some were splashing in off the high diving board which I knew wasn't for me while others were jumping in from the sides which was more my style. Aiming roughly for the middle of the pool and mimicking Tarzan's yodelling just like the others I took a running jump. My feet hit the water and then I had a frightening feeling of going down and down with my mouth wide open giving the last yodel before I finally disappeared. I hadn't quite realised how swimming baths were constructed, sloping gradually down from the shallow water to the deep end.

My flying leap into the pool had taken me closer to the deep end than I had anticipated. Being considerably shorter than most boys of my age I found myself choking on a mouthful of water, at least six inches below the surface. Thankfully, my well-honed instinct of self-preservation kicked in as I began bouncing up and down moving in the direction of the shallow end until slowly and gradually I emerged – coughing, spluttering and gasping for air. I clung on to the side of the baths shivering with cold and fright. Amazingly no one had noticed my plight. Then the thought struck me. I had escaped Hitler's bombs during the war but could so easily have died surrounded by my classmates right here in Morriston baths .

There was worse to come. One more disaster to round off the day. When I eventually recovered from my ordeal of near death by drowning and decided to call it a day, I dragged my shivering body out of the pool, only to be greeted with screams of laughter.

"Look at 'andel mun – 'ee's in the nacker," one lad shouted at the top of his voice as he pointed directly at me.

As I looked down I realised, too late to do anything about it, that my home made swimming trunks, saturated and weighed down with water, were now around my knees. They were so heavy I had some difficulty in pulling them up as I half ran and half hobbled back to the changing rooms.

I swore an oath to myself there and then that I would never return to this or any other swimming baths until I had learned to swim – and I had a decent pair of swimming trunks.

CHAPTER 22

An invitation I couldn't refuse

B oys and girls were strictly segregated at school and any attempt to fraternise just wasn't tolerated. Any boy found near the girls' playground – even loitering around the gates – was severely punished. There was however, one exception to this rule. Two boys from my class were designated as milk monitors and would take it in turns for one week to help in the girls and infants schools. They would carry the crates of milk from the school gates to the classrooms. Unfortunately, when my turn came, I was saddled with Simon.

Milk monitors carried out their duties first thing in the morning during assembly in both the boys and girls schools. This was obviously so that the boys would avoid any contact with the girls. Again there was an exception here. The school had a small nursery and two of the girls were designated to help with the toddlers when they arrived in the morning. One of these was Iris, a well developed, fair-haired girl with blue eyes and a warm smile. She was an obvious choice for this role as she had a very motherly character.

"Teacher says she doesn't want the milk by the door. She wants it over by the window."

Those were Iris's first words to me.

She and her friend Linda were standing, arms folded, by the window. They had watched us struggle into the room carrying the crate of milk which we placed on the floor behind the door as we did

155

in all the classrooms. Now, as 14 year-old boys, we were no match for girls of the same age in the art of flirting.

We were also at a disadvantage because the nursery formed part of the girls' school which meant they were on home ground. We meanwhile were in previously forbidden territory colonised by mysterious creatures. Even the empty classrooms seemed filled with the overwhelming presence of hundreds of girls. And it took the two now confronting us just two days to get us where they wanted – at their beck and call. It was only when we'd completed this manoeuvre that Iris decided to give us the teacher's new instructions. But when these were reversed the following day I suspected it had nothing to do with the teacher at all.

"Oh boys, teacher's changed her mind again. She wants the milk behind the door now," said Iris, smiling ever so sweetly.

However the game was given away by Linda who couldn't resist a cheeky smirk. Still, because they maintained they were passing on instructions from the teacher we had no option but to obey their demands and move the crate of milk back behind the door.

The game the girls were playing was new to me and I felt a little embarrassed, not knowing quite how to react. My shy and nervy companion Simon took the initiative. He beat a hasty retreat from the classroom, with me close on his heels.

I brooded about this for the rest of the day. I just couldn't get Iris's face out of my mind. She and Linda were playing games with us, but I wasn't quite sure whether their intentions were friendly or hostile. I hated the thought that she was being unfriendly or trying to make a fool out of me as I felt very attracted to her. I was sure that Simon would go along with whatever I suggested as long as I took the lead and dealt with the girls. So I planned to get in first when we entered the nursery the following day.

"Right girls," I started, mustering as much authority in my voice as I could, "Where does teacher want the milk today then – behind the door or by the window?"

As usual they were resting against the radiator by the window with their arms folded, smirks on their faces and an air of superiority about them. My words appeared to be unexpected. Linda tightened her arms and gawped at Iris with a look of disbelief that I had the audacity to speak first. Iris recovered her composure quickly and smiling once again she now caught me off guard this time.

"I know your name Handel Swain," she said.

"And I know where you live too – over by the tips."

Simon and I were still standing by the open door holding the crate of milk as she unfolded her arms and strolled over to us.

"Teacher didn't say where she wanted the milk today, Handel."

She ignored Simon and stopped directly in front of me with her hands resting on her hips.

"So just leave it by the door – right," she instructed bossily.

She was standing so close she was almost touching me. I swear I could feel the warmth of her body. I felt intimidated yet overwhelmed by this. She was at least two inches taller than me and probably a little heavier too. Her red woollen cardigan was loosely draped over her shoulders partly covering the plain green dress she wore. I think it was a little on the short side reaching just below her knees. I thought she was magnificent.

The following day – a Friday – was the last day of my milk monitor duty for the girls' and infants schools. It was also the last day Iris would be helping in the nursery. She was constantly on my mind. However, it looked as though my first brush with romance was going to flounder at the nursery door.

I was at a loss to see just how I could maintain contact with this girl who was now consuming all my thoughts. I had no idea where she lived. I had never set eyes on her until a few days before. She wasn't from the top end of the Hafod, or the Pentre where I lived, otherwise I would have seen her in the park. I feared she would be lost to me forever, swallowed up once more in that forbidden world of the girls' school. I was carrying a heavy heart as Simon and I trudged the infant school corridors that last morning. We had delivered the milk as usual, but sadly there was no sign of Iris and Linda. Thinking our brief encounter was over I joined Simon and headed for the gates of the girls' school. He couldn't get away quick enough, glad that his ordeal was finally over, but I lingered a little, desperately hoping to catch one last glimpse of Iris. All of a sudden I heard my name being called.

"Handel! Handel! Over by 'ere."

It was Iris. She was tucked in behind one of the large stone gate pillars waiting for me. She had finished her duties in the nursery and had managed to lose Linda on their way back to the classroom. The urgency in her voice was understandable. We could ill afford the risk of being seen together here.

Her next statement was a little bewildering.

"Handel do you like ice cream?"

She was vigorously nodding her head as she spoke, almost willing me to say yes. Which of course I did.

"Aye mun Iris, I love it. You 'aven't got any 'ave you?"

She had hold of my arm now.

"No, silly," she laughed.

"Now we've got to be quick so listen carefully."

Then she gave her instructions.

"Right, Handel. You go down the prom on Sunday evening and on the way there call in to Toni's cafe and you'll have the best ice cream you've ever tasted. For nothing!"

Then she squeezed my arm and ran back through the school gates.

"Come about seven," she shouted as she went.

My mind was in a whirl as I ran back up the hill to the boys' school. Meeting Iris had been unexpected, but very welcome. Our encounter was brief and our words few which left me with many imponderables. I had to make some sense of what she had said about Sunday evening, Toni's Café, the ice cream and going down the prom.

Pubs and cinemas weren't open on Sundays, so apart from chapel or church, there were very few places where young people could gather. Meeting up with your friends and strolling along the promenade was the thing to do on a Sunday evening.

The experience was even better if you could afford to visit one of the Italian cafes for an ice cream or coffee. So 'going down the prom' was for groups of boys and girls whose sole intention was to size each other up.

Not surprisingly many a loving and lasting marriage owed its origin to a sunny Sunday evening stroll along Swansea's sweeping seafront promenade.

CHAPTER 23

Doing the dirty on little Dinky

Going down to the prom was a Sunday evening pastime that I had yet to experience. Other boys in my class who lived closer to town had often talked about doing this and I thought of tagging along with them as I didn't want to go on my own. But on this occasion I was meeting Iris and I was reluctant for the rest of the boys to know this. I didn't fancy the leg pulling and name calling which might follow if they did get to know of my meeting with her. So I had no alternative but to call on Dinky and persuade him to come along.

The following Sunday was warm and sunny, excellent for an evening stroll along the prom. But first we had to get there. This meant walking right across town, past High Street station; the library in Alexandra Road, on to the Albert Hall cinema; along St Helen's Road before ending up opposite Swansea General Hospital where, I had been informed, Toni's café was.

The walk was around two miles so me and Dinky set off at about six o'clock. I thought this would allow plenty of time to be punctual for my seven o'clock rendezvous with Iris. I must confess that up to this point Dinky was completely in the dark about my intentions that evening. I had neither mentioned Iris nor Toni's Cafe and certainly not the free ice cream. I wasn't sure how he would react so I thought it best to play it by ear and see how things developed. As casually as

I could I simply told him that we were old enough now to try going down the prom and he was really up for it. He did however fire a warning shot across my bows when I first put the proposition to him.

"We must be 'ome by nine mind. You know what happened the last time when we were out late."

He was referring to the time a few years earlier, when we had paid a penny each to take the ferryboat across the River Tawe in an attempt to conquer Kilvey Hill and discover the nesting haunts of what we believed were sparrow hawks and falcons. That penny was all the money we had so to get back home we had to make a long detour down river towards the docks and then into town before heading home. It was an extremely frightening experience and we arrived home very late. This prompted a whacking from Mammy for me which was bad enough, but Dinky received a terrible thrashing from his father.

I assured him that we were not going to make the same mistake again. So off we went in high spirits even though I was feeling a bit guilty that I hadn't been completely honest with him.

Going 'down the prom' meant one thing – boys chasing after girls. As we progressed on our route across town Dinky checked out the reason for our mission.

"Are we going after girls Andy?" he asked.

I hadn't anticipated this. My mind was consumed with the thought of meeting Iris – and the free ice cream – in that order. So I just blurted out the first thing that came into my head which I later came to regret.

"Aye mun," I answered. "If we see any we fancy."

I should have chosen my words more carefully and soon realised that using the word fancy had been a mistake.

"Who do you fancy Andy? Come on mun tell me"

"I don't know mun," I answered.

"We 'aven't seen any yet – 'ave we."

But this didn't shut him up. He was back in a flash.

"I know who you fancy mun," he giggled.

"You're after Daisy Davies."

I hadn't thought of, let alone mentioned, Daisy Davies for ages. She was just a memory from my childhood. But Dinky still believed that one day he and I would have our castle in the country and spend our days riding horses and killing deer with bows and arrows – just like our long time hero Robin Hood.

160

"You know who I fancy Andy," he continued. "I'm goin' to fancy Biddy and you can fancy Daisy Davies. Do you think we'll see 'em?"

These of course were the two girls we were going to carry off when we had found our castle in the country. He continued to ramble on and had become totally preoccupied with the word fancy.

"Do you fancy 'er Andy?" or "What about 'em – do you fancy 'em?" he would ask every time we saw any young girls. At least it helped to pass the time and soon we were at the crossroads where St Helen's Road and Brynymor Road meet. Just a few yards away from the crossroads was Toni's cafe. I glanced up at the hospital clock it was quarter to seven. I was early.

We were a quarter of a mile short of the promenade and Dinky was aware of this. I had to find some way of keeping him on a leash until seven o'clock. At that moment the No. 77 bus, which covered the route from the Guildhall to Morriston and back, pulled in at the bus stop just a few yards away from where we stood. Among those getting off was a noisy cluster of four young girls, one of whom was Iris. She looked very different from the girl I had spoken to in school only days before. Her hair, normally clipped back at the sides, was falling straight, covering her ears. Her face was bright and colourful and I realised as she swept past without noticing me, caught up in the banter with her friends, she was wearing make- up.

I was already a little apprehensive of meeting her in Toni's café, but seeing her now – all painted up and looking so much older – I quickly developed cold feet. I felt unsure of myself. Then my nerve went and I panicked.

"Come on mun Dinky, we're nowhere near the prom," I said, marching off at a fast pace.

But he too had seen the girls. Worse. He had recognised them and couldn't resist spouting the inevitable.

"What about those girls Andy? They're from our school, they are – didn't you fancy 'em."

I tried to ignore him. I needed time to think so just carried on walking away at some speed from the crossroads and Toni's cafe. Dinky was almost running to keep up with me. My mind was in a state of confusion. I had been so wound up during the past couple of days in anticipation of meeting Iris and allowing her to treat me to the free ice cream that I felt ashamed for losing my nerve. My legs however

161

were propelling me forward and within five minutes we were passing the Guildhall with its imposing clock tower. It was only five to seven and there was still plenty of time for me to go back to the café. But my fear of the unknown would not let me – not yet anyway. Dinky could also sense that my attitude had changed since we had seen the girls getting off the bus. If anyone knew me, then he did. We had been best pals for a long time and he questioned me now.

"Why are we 'urrying Andy? I can't keep up with you mun."

I couldn't really answer him so I just said the first thing that came into my head.

"I'm bursting mun – I want a pee. Come on, let's run".

He took me at my word and ran towards the public toilets near the Slip bridge.

I tried to put Iris out of my mind, but I just couldn't erase the picture of her and the other girls getting off the bus. I suppose it was seeing the transformation from the schoolgirl to young woman that had scared me off. I knew one – but not the other. Having Dinky around certainly helped as we stood side by side in the shiny, white tiled public toilet relieving ourselves. This was a rare experience for both of us. In our normal environment around the tips, the canal or the park, if we wanted a pee we would look for the nearest shed or wall. If none of these were available then, after checking to see that there were no adults or girls about, we would proceed. So it came as no surprise when, with a puzzled look on his face Dinky turned to me and asked "Andy, are we in the right place?

"This is the boys' lav – isn't it?"

I laughed and wondered just what he had in his head now.

"Of course it is mun. You don't get these things in girls' lavatories," I said nodding at the white porcelain urinals in front of us.

"Well what about that notice up there?" he inquired, pointing at the sign on the wall above us which he then, laboriously read out.

"Please – adjust – your – dress – before – leaving."

He turned to me again with a dubious look on his face.

"Well I 'aven't got a dress 'ave I?" he said before adding "So we must be in the girls' lav," as he ran out of the building.

I had seen the words before and thought they were a little strange, but realised that what they meant in plain English was 'put your willie away and button your trousers before leaving'. I chased after him and as we emerged from the toilet I shouted a challenge.

"Come on mun I'll race you to the top of the bridge."

We ran towards another Swansea landmark – the iron footbridge that spanned Mumbles Road. It was a fine Sunday evening and there were lots of people strolling along. We raced to the top of the bridge steps where we joined a courting couple who were looking down at the huge floral clock in the gardens below. People were fascinated by this magnificent timepiece, particularly by the movement of its large minute hand. Sixty seconds seemed like an age when gawping down waiting for it to move. It always caught you off guard, jerking forward at the exact moment you blinked, compelling you to wait for another minute to witness any movement. It seemed to have an unspoken curse about it – you dare not move until the clock had moved.

The sun was sinking into the horizon and a cool breeze fanned us as we crossed to the centre of the bridge. Below us was the Slip and on one side of the road was the bus terminus with the halt for the Mumbles Railway on the other. Here the double decker trams of the world's oldest passenger carrying railway stopped on their way from Swansea to the resort of Mumbles.

One of the trams was pulling in as we looked down, click-clacking its way to the halt. Dinky and I had never experienced the pleasure of riding on these and we watched with envy as passengers got on and off. Most would scramble for the seats on the top deck which afforded a grand view of the spectacular curve of Swansea Bay.

We gazed down from the bridge for another 10 minutes or so, watching people coming and going to the entrance of the beach. At this point it was dominated by a large rickety old wooden building where jugs of hot tea could be purchased. Nearby there was a small funfair with swings and roundabouts. I was tempted to forget about going down the prom. The evening I had planned – to see Iris and savour her free ice cream – was in disarray so I decided to let Dinky choose our next move.

"Do you want to go down to the sands, Dinky?" I asked.

He screwed up his face, giving deep thought to the matter.

"No mun. You said we were going down the prom looking for girls," he answered indignantly. With that he ran off again back down the bridge steps and off in the direction of St Helen's rugby ground.

We had never been this far before and were in uncharted territory now. but I was aware that on the other side of the road was the start of the promenade. There were lots of people milling about, some heading for the prom, others heading home with their families. The numbers were swelled as a bus pulled in at the slip disgorging noisy groups of older teenage boys and girls.

"Oo, Andy, I didn't expect all 'ese people mun. It's like being in the shops at Christmas," said Dinky. It was a daft comparison really, but this was the only experience he had of crowds of people moving about, talking, laughing, shouting and enjoying themselves in the breezy sea air and the late evening sunshine.

The smooth tarmac surface of the promenade rose gradually from the road. It was lined on either side by grass and tall trees. About 100 yards along was a large marble column which I later discovered was the Cenotaph. I felt this imposing structure was proof we had at last arrived and were actually on the promenade. But Dinky and I sensed that this was a place for grown-ups and that we were a little out of our depth.

There was no more running or mucking about and we stayed close together observing the people around us. The older boys and girls in separate groups seemed in a hurry and full of the excitement of the unknown. In sharp contrast those young men and women who had paired off, strolled along at a more leisurely pace.

Soon we came across some people gathered around a small memorial dedicated to a dog – Swansea Jack. He was famous for rescuing people from the waters of Swansea Bay and the town's docks many years before. I marvelled at the thought of this amazing dog standing on the seafront overlooking the bay forever guarding the people of the town.

"We must get a dog like 'im when we grow up and 'ave our castle, Andy. We'll need a dog like 'im to guard us," said Dinky, obviously impressed.

Further along a crowd had gathered around an old man who was standing on a platform preaching a sermon. He wasn't wearing a dog collar or cassock and surplice like the vicar at St John's Church did. He was dressed rather scruffily, wearing an old belted raincoat and a bow tie set at a crazy angle. He was short, with a square nose, and a shock of steel-grey hair.

Most people slowed down as they passed, some stopping momentarily to listen. Others had clustered around him. Preaching in a loud and melodic voice he pumped out his message and wasn't phased at all by a group of young men who occasionally heckled him.

"Hey Joe! When's the world coming to an end?" one of them shouted out.

The man answered, not showing any anger at all but with clear conviction in the tone of his voice.

"Sooner than you think young man and you should repent now – before it is too late."

This brought another of the young men into the act.

"Why should he repent Joe? He hasn't done anything wrong."

The old preacher was quick to respond.

"We are all sinners my son – aye – myself included."

The young man didn't let up

"We all know about you Joe, you old rascal. We know you're a sinner – but I'm not."

This brought a chorus of oos and ahs from the crowd. They were probably wondering just how the old man would react to being called a rascal. But he did not get the chance to reply as the first young man repeated his original question.

"You still 'aven't said when the world is going to end Joe."

There was a roar of laughter from the crowd when he added.

"Ask the Lord to wait until after next Saturday Joe – the Swans are playing at home."

There was another burst of laughter then when someone else in the crowd added.

"If you are talking to God about the Swans, Joe, ask him to make sure that they win for a change."

Fortunately the preacher seemed blessed with a sense of humour.

"Well, my son, whenever they do win you can be sure that I've put in a good word for them."

His reply brought cheers from the crowd and some of them even began clapping their hands in appreciation. His sense of humour had defeated the hecklers who were now sloping off. They were not dejected or angry. They accepted that they had come off second best. Then one of them shouted back.

"See you next week Joe."

The old man waved back towards them replying.

"See you next week my son – and God bless you!"

The words seemed to bring to an end this part of the evening's entertainment. The crowd began to disperse with most people making their way back towards the Slip.

Dinky and I continued our trek on the promenade for about another five minutes finally ending up opposite the entrance to Singleton Park. The crowd was thinning out now and many people were turning and heading back to town. With all the excitement of discovering the Cenotaph, the story of Swansea Jack and listening to the preacher – who turned out to be Holy Joe, one of the town's more eccentric characters, we had lost track of time. As we crossed the road suddenly this became uppermost in Dinky thoughts.

"What time is it Andy mun? You know I mustn't be late 'ome."

As he spoke the breeze coming off the sea seemed to develop a chilling edge. We knew what would be waiting for him if he was late. We couldn't see the town hall clock from where we stood and I had no idea of the time. So not wanting to get him into trouble I tapped him on the shoulder and raced off shouting as I went.

"Come on Dinky boy – I'll beat you to The Slip."

Small he might have been but he was nippy on his feet and over a short distance I knew he would catch me, but the Slip was about a quarter of a mile away. I could outpace him over that distance and from there we could get the time from the Guildhall clock.

Eventually, breathless from the race, we reached the public lavatories that had punctuated our journey earlier. It was eight o'clock. Dinky's deadline was nine o'clock as his father was normally back home from the club between nine and half past. So we had at least an hour. From here on we could check the time on clocks of various buildings along the way such as the hospital and the YMCA.

Suddenly, as we hurried past the Guildhall and the hospital came into view a painful thought dawned on me – Iris. She was the very reason I had journeyed to the promenade that night. I wondered whether it was too late to venture into the café. She said I was to be there at seven. I looked up at the hospital clock – it was five minutes past eight. I thought I had a good excuse that would justify my action. I had no money and neither did Dinky. We couldn't just barge in and

166

sit at a table without any money. What if Iris was not available and some other waitress served us? We would be in big trouble then.

All of these thoughts were running through my mind as we approached hospital square. They were excuses, but I knew that my nerve had failed me. My romance with Iris and the free ice cream would never materialise now.

The night was beginning to draw in and there was a chill in the air as we approached the crossroads. The cafe lights had been already switched on and they looked warm and inviting. Hospital Square was still lively, with many people standing around in groups and there was a large queue at the bus stop. Many of the bus routes which criss-crossed town passed through here including the No. 76 from Brynmill to Port Tennant. Toni's café with its bright chandeliers and lace curtains – and Iris – looked particularly inviting as I glanced inside when we passed. It was still busy with most of the tables occupied. There was no sign of her. I was glad because it would have been embarrassing if she had spotted me, yet I was sad because I really did want to see her – never mind tuck in to a free ice cream!

Then Dinky brought me back to reality with a bang. He had gone back to the cafe and was pressing his nose up against the window.

"Oy! Andy. There's a girl in by 'ere from our school mun."

He was telling the whole world, shouting at the top of his voice.

"I thought I recognised her before, when she got off the bus. I told you didn't I," he continued.

His outburst brought a sudden shower of luck on us – good for me, but not so for him.

As I grabbed Dinky and tried to pull him away from the window Iris shot out of the café door. She must have spotted us and reacted with lightning speed. Before I knew what was happening she had both of her arms around my waist and was scolding me.

"Where have you been Handel – you're late. I said to come at seven o' clock."

Her face was lit up. She smiled radiantly and was obviously very glad to see me. I quickly let go of Dinky as she bodily turned me and almost carried me into the cafe. There wasn't a lot of room inside in which to manoeuvre due to the way in which the wooden tables with their sparkling white cloths were packed close together, but she skilfully guided me through them and plonked me down at a small table near the window.

Dinky was left standing outside with a look of bewilderment on his face. Iris looking very pleased had already armed herself with a tray and a cloth and was busy clearing the table and preparing it for her next customer – me!

Dinky had his hands on his hips now and his look of bewilderment turned to one of suspicion. He was glowering at me as he watched Iris clearing the table and generally fussing over me. For a while I pretended not to notice him which was difficult really as he was just inches away with only the window between us.

I waited until Iris had finished preparing the table and vanished with the tray before I plucked up the courage to acknowledge him. He was obviously furious with me as I sat there, a look of complete innocence on my face, shrugging my shoulders to indicate that the sudden arrival of Iris into our lives was as bewildering to me as it was to him. It had all happened in seconds. I honestly believe that Iris wasn't even aware that Dinky and I were together. She soon returned and placed a small silver teaspoon on the table in front of me.

"Now sit there Handel I won't be long – you are in for a real treat," she said with a look of satisfaction on her face.

This momentarily distracted me from my mute confrontation with the unfortunate Dinky.

When Iris disappeared once more I sheepishly turned to look outside – and he was gone.

CHAPTER 24

Ice cream with a sweet kiss on top

Iris was triumphant as she returned to my table carrying a small, circular glass dish on which sat two scoops of vanilla ice cream covered in a chopped pineapple sauce.

"Here it is Handel – a Pineapple Sundae – prepared especially for you," she announced as she glided towards my table. With a flourish she proudly placed it on the table, picked up the spoon and pushed it into my hand. The concoction before me looked so ornate and dainty that I was afraid to spoil it by attacking it with the spoon. I had never seen ice cream presented like this before. I had always believed that it only came in a greaseproof wrapper or at best in a cornet. Iris however was obviously well used to more exotic offerings that ranged from sundaes of all descriptions to the ultimate, mouth-watering Knickerbocker Glory – she served them all.

"Well! Don't just look at it Handel" she scolded.

"Come on – tuck in before it melts."

I honestly felt guilty about Dinky and wondered briefly where he had got to, but eventually directed a polite, half spoon of ice cream towards my mouth.

Satisfied that she had at last got me started Iris left me to enjoy it and tended to her other customers. I could still feel her eyes on me though. It seemed she was anxious to know if I was pleased with her gift. She soon got her answer from the expression on my face as my eyes lit up when the contents of the spoon disappeared into my mouth. The combination of the sweet vanilla cream and the tangy pineapple exploded onto my taste buds. It was a delicious new experience. From that point I forgot about politeness and with heaped spoonfulls I speedily devoured the rest. All too soon the dish was empty and putting down the spoon I sat back in the chair, licked my lips and reflected on my first ever pineapple sundae.

Iris who was serving a young couple with coffee at a table near the centre of the cafe looked across at me. The broad smile on her face told me she was happy and filled with pride. It was only then that a thought struck me – who was going to pay for the delicious ice cream I had just consumed? And why, I wondered, was Iris looking so pleased with herself? After all I was the one who enjoyed the delicious sundae – not her. I was feeling a little apprehensive now as I didn't really understand what she had meant by a free ice cream when she had first issued her invitation.

It was only then that I began to focus on the other customers who were paying their bills to a large, thick set man who I assumed was the owner – Toni. He was sitting at the cash desk near the front door. I had no idea what the cost of the pineapple sundae was and even if I did I didn't have a brass farthing on me with which to pay for it. The cafe was emptying quickly by now. It was three-quarters full when I had first entered, but now more than half of the people had left. Iris and the three other waitresses were busy dashing about clearing and cleaning the tables, mine included.

I was beginning to feel a little conspicuous sitting there all alone as the tables around me emptied. When they finished their ice creams or coffees, customers got up, paid their bills and left. Common sense told me that this was precisely what I should do too. It was probably only five minutes or so but it seemed like an age since I had finished the pineapple sundae and I now faced a dilemma – should I get up and walk out which would mean having to pass the cash desk and Toni, who might demand payment or should I sit there and wait for some sort of signal from Iris. I was completely in her hands.

I did neither, but instead stared at the table trying not to think of the fate I was convinced was about to befall me. My imagination was running riot. I could see Iris abandoning me, with the certain outcome being a confrontation with Toni who was angrily demanding payment.

Then I was consumed by panic for when I looked up I discovered that Iris had disappeared. Only moments earlier the four waitresses were busy clearing the tables, now only the older girl remained. Iris and the other two were nowhere to be seen.

The young couple that Iris had served earlier got up from their table and made their way to the cash desk. My eyes followed them across the room and as I watched them paying their bill I found myself looking straight at Toni. As our eyes met he gave a slight nod, smiled broadly and winked at me. I felt embarrassed but thankfully before I could decide exactly what it was all about Iris and the other two girls emerged once more, dressed in their coats. They made straight for the cash desk with Iris calling me over to join her. The three of them clustered around Toni laughing and chatting with him; holding out their hands into which he placed so many coins – their wages. And almost in unison the three of them called out as Iris grabbed my arm and whisked me towards the door.

"Thank you Toni. See you next week – goodnight."

"Goodnight girls," he responded "Be good now."

Then finally with a low chuckle – he shouted.

"And you Handel – you be a good boy, too."

I could still hear Toni chortling away as Iris, giggling along with the other girls pushed me through the door to the street. There were two lads waiting there for her friends. I didn't recognise either of them and they looked older than me.

"So long Iris," the two girls shouted as they joined the boys. Then, linking arms with them, they hurried off in the direction of the promenade and the beach. My destination had already been decided. Iris shepherded me across the road as a No. 77 bus approached.

"Come on Handel – here's our bus," she said.

We joined the queue as it pulled in to the bus stop opposite the café. Queuing at bus stops always seemed to develop into some kind of battle, with the people at the front of the queue always trying to board the bus before those alighting could do so, and those at the back of the queue compounding things by pushing forward in their eagerness to get on.

Buses were the most common form of transport and very often at peak times the conductor would shout the dreaded words "Standing room only." It wasn't so bad this evening though, just a minor skirmish before Iris and I installed ourselves on the upper deck. She sat on the inside, clasping my arm tightly and holding me close.

Except for my sisters I had never sat as close as this to a girl before in my life and added to the evenings previous exploits it was quite thrilling. I did have one niggling concern though. I was sitting on a bus but lacking the necessary penny for the fare. I was glad that we were sitting so tightly together as I put my face close to her and, not wanting anyone else to hear – especially the conductor – whispered to her.

"Iris! I 'aven't got any money mun. I can't pay the fare."

"Don't worry Handel," she said opening her hand to reveal a pile of coins. We work from seven until half past eight and Toni pays us a shilling an hour. That's one and six and I get even more than that in tips. Look Handel! I've got more than three and six here so I can pay for both of us."

Three shillings and sixpence was a tidy sum for a young girl and no doubt her earnings at the cafe helped to pay for her smart new coat along with the make-up she was wearing – lipstick, rouge and a heady scent. Then it struck me that she had probably paid for the ice cream.

"The ice cream was smashing Iris. I really enjoyed that," I blurted out without thinking.

"Pineapple sundae you said it was. How much did that cost then?"

"Didn't cost me anything mun," she said. "I told you, it's free. They cost ninepence each, but Toni lets us have one free ice cream a night for our boyfriends. So if you come next week you can have another one."

She had just declared that I was her boyfriend, well at least for tonight, so if I went to the cafe again next Sunday I would be her boyfriend then too.

All of this was a lot to take in during such a short time. I was enjoying the evening, sitting there in the bus feeling the warmth of Iris close to me. It didn't take me long to come to the conclusion that to be Iris's boyfriend was not a bad thing at all, but I decided that for the moment I wouldn't tell anyone not even Dinky, with whom I usually shared all of my secrets, anything about my exploits.

The bus had completed its journey through the town and we were approaching Hafod Bridge which was two stops before the Mexico Fountain pub where I would normally get off, but Iris was nudging me with her arm and leg, urging me to move.

172

"Come on Handel, up you get mun – this is my stop."

As we were leaving the bus I recognised the back of a familiar figure running along Neath Road. It was Dinky. The bus journey would have taken about 15 minutes so I reckoned that it must be about ten to nine now. He should be home in five minutes, well before his nine o'clock deadline to beat his father home from the club. Iris was walking quickly, hurrying me along as we crossed over the bridge which formed part of the main road. There was a sharp left hand turn leading to a slope which took us down to Cwm Road. As we hurried down the slope I thought that she probably had a deadline too, her parents wanting her safely home by nine or half-past nine at the latest.

At the bottom of the slope we turned left again and headed under the arch below the bridge where she stopped.

"I only live around the corner Handel, you must say goodnight to me here – right," she said unlocking her arm from mine and turning to face me. She took my arms and placed them around her waist pulling me close to her. My nose was just about level with her chin and as I looked up at her face I saw that she had closed her eyes. I was ninety per cent certain that I was being invited to kiss her, but once more I lost my nerve. So Iris had to take the initiative again. When I had not responded as she expected she cupped one hand behind my neck and kissed me on my cheek. Then gently she lowered my head to rest on her breast. In my dreams I had been in this situation many times. In reality I was lost. With my blood racing, the only response I could muster was to hold on to Iris as tightly as I could. I would have stayed like this for an eternity, the two of us locked in a breathtaking embrace, each reluctant to let the other go. Even though my arms and back ached due to our awkward stance I was determined to cling on to her as long as she would let me. All too soon she relaxed her hold. Then she kissed me once more, this time on my forehead.

"I must go Handel – my father will be out looking for me," she said in a soft whisper.

The thought of her father suddenly appearing on the scene soon cooled my ardour as I quickly released my embrace and stepped back. My experience with fathers – my own and Dinky's in particular put me on my guard immediately. Surprised by my sudden movement she laughed and took hold of my hands once more pulling me close.

173

"It's all right Handel, he won't mind you he's not going to eat you. He just worries about me – that's all," she said reassuringly.

I didn't want her to go, but I could see that she was becoming anxious as she released my hands and delved into her handbag. She pulled out a small package, placed it in my hand before she was off.

"Look out for me in school tomorrow – and don't forget next Sunday," she called as she turned and waved to me.

Iris was already fifteen, six months older than me and in a couple of weeks she would be leaving school and starting work. She hadn't found a job yet, but was hoping that with her experience of working at Toni's she might become a waitress at one of the town's restaurants or cafes. I had no idea where she lived other than that she had headed towards the cobbled surface of The Strand which led down to the lower part of the town. It was mainly a commercial district with no houses as far as I knew. Opposite Kramsky's rag and bone yard there was a sharp bend to the left, leading back to the Hafod, which she quickly disappeared around.

When she was out of sight I looked down at the palm of my hand and nestling there was a small packet of Woodbine cigarettes. By giving me these I felt she was confirming that I was indeed her boyfriend. Most girls didn't smoke but thought that it was grown up and manly if their boyfriends did. Personally I had mixed feelings about smoking. Having tried the occasional cigarette with Dinky and the rest of the gang I didn't like the smell or taste of the smoke and tobacco one bit. I'm sure the others felt the same but like me they would never admit that. If we followed our elders then smoking was indeed the thing to do as you grew up. So I would just have to persevere and hope that in time I too gained pleasure from it.

CHAPTER 25

Smoking like a movie gangster

Dinky had been my best friend for years. But all that we had been through together counted for little after he had been left to walk home alone on the night of my first meeting with Iris. We had endured many quarrels during our long friendship so although I felt guilty about the incident I was quite sure that within a couple of days we would bump into each other and eventually things would be alright again. But that wasn't to be. I didn't see him on the Monday or Tuesday following our trek down to the prom and, as the days passed, so the nagging guilt I felt about persuading him to come with me in pursuit of Iris without telling him increased. By Wednesday I could stand it no longer so I went round to his house and knocked on his front door.

The news wasn't good. It was soon obvious that Dinky was having none of it. I think he was waiting for me, with a speech all prepared. As he opened the door we came face to face.

"I'm not playing with you any more," he blurted out. "You went with that girl and had ice cream. I saw you and you left me to go 'ome by myself. So you can stick your ice cream where the monkey sticks his nuts."

With that he stuck out his tongue, told me in no uncertain terms that he was no longer my best friend and slammed the door in my face. For a while I stood there. Speechless. I felt I had been harshly

judged. It wasn't my fault. I was sure that if he had been in my position he would have done exactly the same. It was not often that you had the chance of getting a girl – and a free ice cream. In retaliation I stormed off, vowing never to speak to him again and shouting at the now closed door that he could stick his friendship in exactly the same place he had told me to stick my ice cream.

There was better news as far as Iris was concerned. Although we never spoke at school I did see her a few times when I looked down into the girls' playground. I gave a sly little wave when I was sure no one was looking and she smiled back at me. Then on Friday afternoon of that week, a small boy from one of the junior classes approached me in the playground and pushed a folded piece of paper in my hand. When I opened it up it read 'Come for ice cream at a quarter past eight on Sunday' It was a note from Iris and below the message was a crude drawing of a heart bearing the letters H & I with an arrow through it. I stuffed it into my trouser pocket as quickly as I could, hoping that no one else had noticed. I later found out the little boy who had delivered it was Iris's younger brother. The clandestine exchange had cost her a penny she informed me later.

Time dragged as I waited impatiently for Sunday evening to arrive. Even my weekly Saturday night visit to Maggie's and the treats she had in store lacked some of their usual appeal. I thought back to the previous Sunday, imagined the pleasures to come, and dreamed about Iris. The thought of having another pineapple sundae was in the forefront of my mind too, but delicious as it was I had decided that the ice cream was now definitely second best.

At last Sunday afternoon arrived. Mam as usual had baked something special for tea – rhubarb tart and custard. It was delicious, but didn't compare to the delights of a pineapple sundae. As I left the house later I was tingling with excitement and brimming with confidence. I was so sure of myself as I made my way down the rough slope from the school to Cwm Road that I stopped and lit up one of the Woodbines that Iris had given me the week before. I puffed away for a while, trying to inhale some of the smoke, which resulted in a fit of coughing and feeling of giddiness. I had seen boys of ten dragging on cigarettes better than me and inhaling the smoke like gangsters in the movies. Thinking how daft I was and that I'd never get the hang of it I threw the half-smoked cigarette away. Once again I had failed.

I decided to head past the spot under Hafod Bridge where Iris and I had been locked in our embrace the previous Sunday. Although I was excited at the thought that we would soon be there again I had an overwhelming desire to find out where she lived. I was in the lower part of the Hafod where there were several rows of houses going back as far as the railway line. She probably lived somewhere in there I thought. I wanted to go further but was checked by the thought that this might be an intrusion if she spotted me and I didn't want anything to spoil our relationship now.

Satisfied that I now had at least some idea of where she lived I continued down The Strand. This had once been a flourishing riverside area, but there was now a sense of decay about the place with many run down and derelict buildings. The only thriving businesses were those of the rag bone and scrap metal merchants occupying the arches underneath Prince of Wales Road. As it was a Sunday afternoon it was quiet with few people about. Further along there was a narrow side road leading up to a bridge where I crossed over the main railway line before emerging by the Palace Theatre on the fringe of the town centre. From there I took a different route to the previous week when I was accompanied by Dinky. In my eagerness to see Iris I was early and had time to kill, so I continued straight down High Street, one of the main shopping areas of the town. Surprisingly there were quite a few people about although again because it was Sunday the only shopping they could do was window shopping.

I too looked in the windows at the wares of businesses like those of Morgan and Lott the furnishers, Lesley's stores, the Star Supply Store where Maggie worked and opposite it, the pride of the street – the department store of Lewis Lewis and of course lower down Woolworths. There was also the Mackworth Hotel and pubs such as the Tenby, the Bush and the Kings Arms. They too were all closed of course as it was Sunday.

I turned right into the remains of College Street and headed into what was the heart of the town until it had been flattened by the German bombers in their wartime blitz. I had timed my walk to arrive at Hospital Square about quarter to seven – the same time as the previous week. Iris's bus would be pulling in shortly and I couldn't resist the temptation to take a quick peek at her when she got off. I positioned myself on the opposite corner of the square where I hoped I could see her, but she would not see me. Sure enough within a couple of minutes the bus had arrived and I got my reward. Just a fleeting glimpse, but worth it, as chatting and giggling she and her friends got off and disappeared into Toni's Cafe.

I had over an hour's wait so I decided that I would cover the same ground as I had the previous week. I made my way down to the prom, had a pee in the public lavatories, looked at the plaque com-memorating Swansea Jack, before going on to the Cenotaph. When I reached here the usual crowd had gathered to listen to Holy Joe. I stopped and listened to him and the banter from the crowd for a while then carried on to the end of the prom before doubling back to the Slip. From here I could see the town hall clock.

It was still only half past seven. The walk along the prom was not half as much fun as the previous week when Dinky had been with me. I crossed the road and then the railway before ambling down on to the beach. The tide was out and some boys were kicking a ball about on the firm sand just below the high tide line. The sunny weather had attracted the usual crowds to this favoured part of the beach but by now only the stragglers were left, packing up before heading home. I trudged heavily through the dry sand making my way down to the iron bridge that spanned the Mumbles Road, wistfully imagining the delights to come – being with Iris and of course another delicious pineapple sundae.

But there was also something else on my mind. I was having increasing pangs of guilt about how I had used Dinky. In all of our previous quarrels it was only a matter of days before we had made it up. I hadn't seen him since our doorstep confrontation on Wednesday and I wondered just what I had to do to regain his trust. As I crossed the Slip bridge I looked down to the floral clock below. To my surprise it was showing ten past eight. As can often happen when you have time to kill, I had overdone it, and would need to hurry if I was to get to Toni's Cafe – and Iris – at quarter past.

Perhaps it was just as well that I was a little late. I had no time to be apprehensive. I was a little out of breath when I finally got inside where thankfully Iris was waiting for me. She whisked me away once again to a table near the window. I glanced at Toni as I passed the cash desk – he was full of smiles and winks. The pineapple sundae tasted even better than the previous week probably because I was more relaxed – safe in the knowledge that it was a gift from Toni.

In contrast to the earlier part of the evening the remainder flew by. Iris and I were soon under the arch of Hafod Bridge locked in a fervent embrace. This time, I didn't hesitate in putting my lips to hers, if a little awkwardly, as she leaned towards me and closed her eyes. I was pleasantly surprised that once I had taken the initiative Iris responded. Her lips opened slightly and I could feel her warm breath. Then pulling me ever tighter to her breast it developed into a deeper, more sensual kiss.

They say you never forget your first real kiss and in my case perhaps it had something to do with the length of time it took to complete. Only sheer exhaustion would have broken our frantic embrace as neither of us wanted it to end. But end it did and rather abruptly when a faint yet distinct voice broke the silence "Iris! Iris! Is that you – under the bridge there?"

179

I was already up on my toes, ready to do a runner as she confirmed my worst fears.

"Oh, it's my father," she whispered.

She must have sensed the fear that gripped me because she pulled me close to her once more and called back to her father.

"I'm coming dad – coming now."

There was no fear or panic on her part as she whispered once more to reassure me.

"Don't worry Handel, he's just an old fusspot but I'd better go."

We embraced once more pressing our bodies and lips together for a final goodnight kiss. Then she hurried off, the clip-clop of her high-heels echoing under the bridge as she shouted back to me.

"See you in school tomorrow."

I did see her the following day and again on the Tuesday, but there was always the barrier between the boys' and girls' playgrounds keeping us apart. By Wednesday I went looking for her young brother, armed with a penny and a note for Iris.

'Can we have a date – under the bridge – seven o'clock, Thursday?' it said simply.

I wasn't prepared to wait for another whole week before seeing her again. The answer came at playtime the following day when I looked down to the girls' playground only to be greeted by Iris smiling and vigorously nodding her head.

Eager to be with her I arrived early. She must have felt the same way as she was already waiting for me. Unlike our Sunday night trysts when there were few people about and darkness beckoning, the scene around Hafod Bridge on this fine summer's evening was quite different. Some boys were kicking a ball about on Cwm Road and gangs of kids of all ages scurried about chasing after each other and generally living out their own particular fantasies.

We sat on the wall at the bottom of the slope leading down from Prince of Wales Road. It would have been hopeless if we had tried to hide ourselves under the bridge as we had before. We would have been like a magnet, drawing every child in the district with their natural curiosity to gawp at a young courting couple. It was embarrassing enough with the occasional wolf whistles we were getting, but we didn't mind. We were together, sitting close, hardly speaking a word, but with our hands gently touching.

This was just as well and lucky for us that we had arrived early as fifteen minutes later a man walking along with a little lad, who I recognised as Iris's brother, emerged from under the bridge.

My first thought as I pulled my hand away from Iris was 'It's her father and brother' and the second 'The little beggar has given us away.' And I had paid him a penny too! Iris was motionless at my side. I dare not look at her. My eyes were fixed firmly on her father and brother as they walked towards us.

Not knowing just what to expect or how to react I became a little jittery as they came closer. But strangely they ignored us, walking past and on up the slope to the main road. It was only when they had reached the top that her father turned round and called back in a rather matter of fact way.

"Your Mam says don't be late Iris – supper's nearly ready."

Iris giggled and grabbed my hand again.

"Don't worry about my father Handel," she said. "I told you he's just fussy, that's all."

She stood up then and I could tell from the tone of her voice that our courting for that evening was over.

"My Mam is different mind," she added.

"She won't stop nagging if I'm late for my supper, so see you on Sunday – right."

We held hands as our lips touched tenderly, but briefly, and then she was gone.

I am so glad now that I had plucked up enough courage to arrange the date with her that evening as sadly it was the very last time that I ever saw Iris. Our short-lived but wonderful courtship was brought to end not by Iris's father or her mother or anyone else for that matter. Instead our love was to be smothered three days later – by a bug.

The following Saturday I developed a rash which Dr Nancy Evans who examined me diagnosed as German measles. On her instructions I was to be isolated immediately and put into strict quarantine. I didn't realise then, but by the time that I had made a full recovery the school summer holidays had started and Iris had left school for good.

Our romance had been brief, but those heady days truly were Pineapple Sundays.

CHAPTER 26

Measles, misery and making up

German measles or rubella, was not as common as ordinary measles, chicken pox or mumps, diseases that most families experienced. As a result, a lot of myths and old wives tales were associated with it. From the time that the rash was first discovered on my body I can honestly say that apart from Mam, the rest of my family kept their distance. In fact they treated me as if I had leprosy. I was strictly off limits, confined to one bedroom – the one used by Mam and Molly – with the curtains drawn. This was necessary as apparently there was some danger to the sufferer's eyesight if exposed to strong sunlight. It also appeared that it was worse for women to suffer this ailment as both Molly and Maggie were kept well away from me. I can't recall suffering any real pain from German measles but spent probably two of the most miserable weeks of my life all alone in a darkened bedroom, pining for Iris.

Although by now we had electric light in all the rooms of the house, Mam still had to watch the pennies and was sparing with the amount of time I could indulge in my favourite pastime of reading. Evenings and weekends when I could hear my younger brothers Walter and Eddie coming and going and the general noise of other children playing outside, were particularly bad. But the worst time of all was Sunday evening when I should have been meeting Iris at Toni's Cafe and enjoying a pineapple sundae. There was no way I could communicate with her and I wondered just how she felt when I failed to turn up. I conjured up all sorts of pictures in my mind. I could see her travelling home on the bus alone, sad and downcast, believing that I no longer cared. Worse still, I could imagine her being angry with me and seeking out another boy to enjoy her favours. It was two weeks of torture and I longed for it to end. Of course, because I never saw her again I would never learn just how she did react. I later realised of course that because of our intimate relationship she too might have been suffering just like me.

Strangely some good news did come about to cheer me up during what I regarded as one of the most horrible times of my life. It was something that I was particularly glad about. Dinky had heard about my illness and wanted to speak to me. When he called at the house however I still had two days of my confinement to go before being allowed out, so Mam, sticking strictly to the rules, would not allow him in. However she did agree that I could speak to him from the bedroom window as long as we kept the conversation short and I shielded my eyes from the sun. To help me achieve this she gave me a magazine which I had to hold above my head, and follow her strict instructions that I was not to lean out of the window otherwise I would be struck down by lightning.

As much as I wanted to see and speak to Dinky I took heed of her strongly worded advice. I wasn't going to take any chances and risk damaging my eyesight. It was nearly a month since he had told me to stick my ice cream where the monkey sticks his nuts. We had never quarrelled for this length of time before. It was hard to admit but it was my fault really and I should have tried harder to patch things up with him. At the time though, I was so smitten with Iris that I didn't think about anything or anyone else, so I was glad that he had finally come to see me. Knowing Dinky and his vivid imagination, fired up with tales of people with German measles going blind, I would bet that there was also a hint of morbid curiosity in his visit. My thoughts on this were confirmed when he saw me appearing at the open window shielding my face with the magazine.

"Are you blind Andy? Can you see me?" he shouted, standing on tip toe as if the extra inch or so would help him to see me better. Immediately I seized on his remarks and his pathetic demeanour. I needed all the sympathy points I could muster to get back in his good books. This was too good an opportunity to miss.

Now there is an art to telling lies which I found extremely difficult to master, but I was a good actor, and with the added bonus that he couldn't see my face anyway due to the magazine covering most of it, I responded to his question by pretending that I couldn't see him.

"Is that you Dinky?" I said slowly, in a weak and feeble voice, dragging out every syllable.

"I can't see you mun. Where are you?"

I'm sure he was half-expecting this, as all excited and wound up, he shouted back.

"I'm down by 'ere Andy mun – outside your back door."

I dared not show my face as he would have seen through me straight away, but I pushed my hand out through the window, poking at the air as if I was feeling for something, but didn't utter a word.

I think my play-acting frightened him. He began jumping up and down, becoming emotional and yelling.

"Look down Andy mun – look down by 'ere."

Taking the risk of overdoing it, I couldn't resist the temptation to pretend I couldn't hear him as well as not see him.

"Mam! Mam! Where is Dinky?" I said, again in a slow and deliberate voice.

"You said Dinky was coming to see me."

What I hadn't reckoned with was that Mam was standing just inside the back door, no doubt a little confused and wondering what was going on to get Dinky all worked up and jumping up and down.

"Mrs Swain! Mrs Swain! Andy can't see me and 'e can't 'ear me either," he was yelling at the top of his voice.

I was not expecting this and had to think quickly when she appeared alongside Dinky. Straight away she shouted up at me.

"Handel! What are you up to? Now speak to Dinky. For just one minute mind, then close the window."

I regained my eyesight, speech and hearing immediately. It was miraculous as far as Dinky was concerned, when I shouted back.

"Oh, I can see you now Dinky boy. It must have been the light affecting my eyes."

It seemed my little bout of play-acting had paid off. I had won a reprieve and got my sympathy points. Suddenly Dinky bubbled over.

"I didn't know you were bad Andy, 'onest mun. I only found out today. I've been looking for you everywhere – up the tip, over the park, down the canal, in school, everywhere, but I couldn't find you."

There was probably some truth in this, but he would have known about my illness well before that day. I bet his curiosity had got the better of him and he couldn't wait until I recovered. He just had to find out if I was blind. Anyway I was in a good position now so I thought I'd rub it in. Holding the magazine over my face I moaned.

"Ohhhh – I've been very bad mun Dinky, in terrible pain I've been. In my bones, in my 'ead. I couldn't eat. Mam had to feed me, I thought I was dying – 'onest mun." He didn't like me moaning on about how ill I had been and quickly changed the subject.

"Andy! your Mam will be shouting at us in a minute. When are you going to get better and come out to play again."

Before I could respond Mam emerged from the kitchen and answered the question for me.

"Saturday, Dinky. Doctor Evans said he can go out for a little time on Saturday. So off you go and we'll see you Saturday, right."

"Right Mrs Swain" he answered and before running off he shouted.

"I'm glad you're not blind Andy."

Saturday turned out to be a fine summer's day. Dinky came around early and although we didn't venture far from the house Mam seemed quite satisfied that I was fully recovered, allowing me to play outside for most of the day.

I felt relieved that Dinky and I were best friends once more. As long as he was around to keep my mind occupied there was less time for me to brood about Iris. It was a good start not just for my recovery from German measles, but the long summer holidays. I was aware that this would be the last time for me to enjoy such a luxury as by this time the following year I would be working.

I felt fit and well and I was determined that on the following day – Sunday – I was going to slip away in the late afternoon after tea. I wanted to see Iris so I was going down to the prom. But fate conspired against me. Once more I was confined to the house – this time by the weather. After a fine morning it began to rain, so after tea that Sunday instead of going down the prom I sat by the window in the front room looking out across the square to the Great Tip. The whole world seemed shrouded in a misty cloak of fine rain. It was graveyard quiet, a world bereft of children. Even Tom the car was absent from the garage across the road where he was still lovingly restoring his Standard 10 car.

There is no more miserable a time for a fourteen year-old boy than a wet Sunday afternoon at the start of the summer holidays. Normally on such days as these I would have been content to sit there with my head in a book. I was very much into the books of Charles Dickens then and had just started reading Great Expectations. But somehow on this wet day I didn't quite fancy the company of Pip and Estella or Miss Haversham. I sorely missed Iris. Like the weather I was in a depression, gripped in a vice of melancholy and lovelorn stupor. I needn't have worried as the lift my depressed spirit so badly needed was on its way that very afternoon. Molly's fiancé Sid – she insisted on him being called her fiancé as they were now engaged to be married – had decided that as I would soon be working it was time for me to graduate from reading the works of Dickens, Kipling and Conan Doyle, which he considered to be old fashioned and thrill to the exciting new adventures of ace Yanky news reporter Hank Jansen. My dreams of conquering the jungles of Africa and South America or sailing the seven seas were now to be exchanged for the seedy, underworld life of the City of Chicago.

Hank Jansen was an amazing character. A daring, fearless crusader who smoked Philip Morris cigarettes, always had a crumpled hundred dollar bill or 'C' note as he called it, stuck in his top pocket and worked as a reporter for the Chicago Daily Tribune. Single-handedly he took on the mob, corrupt politicians and big corporations. He was always getting into scrapes with his adversaries or their henchmen who would lay in wait for him or lure him to remote places. There they would set upon him beating him to near-death, before he would finally find the strength to recover and with his trusted fists despatch them to oblivion. He was a constant thorn in the side of his editor because of the risks he took, but like the Mounties he always got his man – and his story.

Of course Jansen's adventures were heavily laced with broads – tall leggy blondes or dark sultry brunettes, sweet innocent maidens or hardened voracious harlots. They were all the same to him as they inevitably succumbed to his rugged good looks and fatal charm. The stories would go on at some length exploring every detail about these encounters. They opened up an entire new world for this fourteen year-old who generally wouldn't be seen dead near the romantic rubbish of the girls books and magazines that his sisters coveted.

The Hank Jansen books were bestsellers, reputedly selling in millions. He was a prolific writer turning out a new book every month. Sid was an ardent fan and had a copy of every one of them. He promised that if I enjoyed reading the first book then he would let me borrow the others. But it came with a proviso that I was not to lend the books to anyone else and it would be better not to show them to Mam.

Consequently, over the next year or so, as long as I had access to the books, most of my reading was done secreted away in the bedroom or in the lavatory and, when the weather permitted, behind the sheds near the tip or on a bench in the park. Whenever the book was not clenched between my sweaty little hands it was kept hidden away under the mattress of my bed.

Until then I had not given much thought to what kind of job I would have when I left school the following year. My original plan or at least the ambition Mam had for me of becoming a teacher, had come to nothing as I had failed the scholarship examination. I had declined Mam's offer of attending Gregg's College and follow in the footsteps of my brother Daniel, so the idea within the family was to try and secure an apprenticeship for me, but these were not easy things to come by. Learning a trade was still very much for the privileged sons of existing tradesmen. Sam, Maggie's husband was a tradesman. He was an only child and no doubt the apprenticeship was secured largely due to the efforts of his formidable mother, Mrs Bennett. She was streetwise and had all the necessary connections with people of influence. Mam on the other hand, with her family background in farming, was not really of much use in this respect. She would as ever though try her best and explore every avenue. At her instigation feelers were put out and the word spread around that there was a bright young lad, a good all-rounder at school, seeking an apprenticeship.

However having followed religiously the exploits of my hero Hank Jansen I had ideas of my own. There were no doubts in my own mind where my future lay. My dreams and fantasies now were of Handel Swain – ace reporter – fighting corruption and injustice, smoking Philip Morris cigarettes with a crumpled C-note stuck in my top pocket – and getting laid by the broads.

CHAPTER 27

In the swim,
but out of luck

Apart from reading Hank Jansen books, the early part of the summer holidays passed rather tediously. My recovery from German measles allowed me plenty of time to think of Iris and on the first Sunday I was able to, I retraced my steps through the town down to hospital square. Arriving well before seven o'clock I was hoping to see Iris getting off the bus and making her way to Toni's cafe. It had been a fine summer's day unlike the previous wet and washed-out Sunday. When the bus eventually arrived at the bus stop it was packed. Almost half of the passengers got off and for a brief moment my hopes were raised for among them, chattering and giggling, were a couple of groups of young girls. Sadly, Iris was nowhere to be seen.

I waited half an hour for the next bus, keenly scrutinising each and every face as the passengers got off, but there was still no sign of her. Not wanting to give up I crossed the road and walked slowly past Toni's Café. I glanced inside trying not to draw attention to myself, but still hoping that Iris would see me just as she had on that first memorable night. Toni could clearly be seen sitting at the cash desk and I caught a glimpse of the full-time waitress, but failed to recognise anyone else. It seemed clear that I wasn't going to see Iris. When passion and love take their hold common sense can desert you and for the next half an hour I wandered aimlessly around hospital square hoping for a miracle. I even went as far as looking for her in the other cafes in the area, thinking that she might have changed her job. Eventually, shortly after eight o'clock, knowing that there would be no bus ride home for me that night I dejectedly made my way home.

The following day, the start of the third week of the August school holidays, the waters of Swansea Bay had warmed up sufficiently to encourage even the most reluctant of bathers to dip their toes into the scummy, oil-laden sea. Swansea was a major port for the handling of crude oil destined for nearby Llandarcy refinery. As a result the water in and around the docks had a fair percentage of oil mixed in with it. Winter storms churning up the tides did help to disperse it. Now, at the height of summer, with its normal placid seas, taking a dip in the bay was not the wisest of moves if you failed to have access to a hot bath afterwards. At the time I believed that the seas of the entire world were just as bad. It was not until I had the pleasure of bathing off Mumbles, just five miles away that I discovered how clean the sea could be.

Dinky and I were meeting Maggie's husband Sam on the beach near where he worked in the docks. On Maggie's instructions he was going to teach us to swim. She had been worried by my exploits at Morriston swimming baths earlier in the year so she had decided it was time that I learned how to master the art of survival in the water. Dinky, who wasn't all that partial to water, agreed after a great deal of encouragement from his mother, that it would be good for him too.

We met Sam at about five o'clock on the beach near the west pier. Low tide exposed a large area of sludge and mud in Swansea Bay, but mercifully as we took to the water it was at about the half way mark and coming in. Most people preferred to swim a mile or so further along near the Slip so this part of the beach was fairly clear.

Sam was an excellent swimmer. I expect he needed to be, working as he did in the docks, and having spent his National Service with the Royal Navy. I was quite sure that at this time of day he would have preferred to be heading home for his dinner instead of having to spend an hour or so teaching two youngsters how to swim. Like me, however, he had received his instructions from Maggie and both of us knew that it was useless to argue with her once she had set her mind on something. Not that I needed much persuading. Apart from the fact that being able to swim might one day save my life I was also one of the few in my class who couldn't. Bearing in mind my competitive nature and my desire always to be among the best, my failure to master swimming rankled. I hated being in the shallow end of the baths when most of the boys congregated near the deep end.

According to Sam the breaststroke was the quickest and easiest to master and it was surprising how quickly Dinky and I got to grips with it. Probably the hardest part, like learning to ride a bike, was gaining enough confidence to go it alone. Sam helped keep us afloat at first, holding his hand under our chests, but by the end of the first lesson we had both managed to keep going under our own steam, if only for a couple of strokes.

The feeling of exhilaration that this new found freedom in the water gave us grew by the day as our lessons with Sam continued. By the end of the week, even though the weather had deteriorated, bringing some light rain, we were unstoppable. It even came to the point where Sam had to threaten to leave us and go home on his own in a bid to get us out of the water. Dinky was all fired up, now that he could swim. He was going on his annual holiday to his grandparents in Weston-super-Mare that weekend and he just couldn't wait to surprise his English cousins with his breast stroke.

His delight faded that evening however when he discovered that as he was heading for England, the love of his life – Biddy Roberts – was travelling in the opposite direction on her way to stay with Mrs Gwen Evans, her granny in Swansea.

Alarmed by this news he came banging on our kitchen door early on Saturday morning, pleading with me to convince Biddy of his undying love. Brammer, his rival for Biddy's affection, had told him he was going to be Biddy's boyfriend now. So Dinky decided it was my job to thwart Brammer and not allow him a free rein during his absence. I was to see Biddy as soon as she arrived and before Brammer could contact her. Dinky said her father was bringing her down in his car and they would be arriving at dinner time.

Frankly I was more than a little suspicious of his motive. I was not quite sure whether he had actually informed Biddy of his love and if the threat from Brammer was real. He said he was banking on me to do this small favour for him, but I believed he was getting me to do his dirty work, telling her that he fancied her and hoping for the best. But he was my pal and I still had pangs of guilt whenever I recalled the way I had used him on our first trip to the prom, an episode that had hurt him, so I gave him my word I'd speak to Biddy – especially after he made me cross my heart and swear to die.

That afternoon, fortified with my usual Saturday dinner of laverbread and cockles, I walked the hundred yards or so to Mrs Gwen Evans' house. Parked outside was a huge Humber saloon indicating that Biddy had arrived. Unfortunately that is the point at which my courage deserted me. I couldn't think of an excuse to knock on the door and ask for Biddy and wasn't looking forward to confronting her father either. For the next half an hour I paced up and down Odo Street trying not to look conspicuous, hoping – in vain as it turned out – for Biddy to appear. Then, just as I was about to give up my vigil someone did emerge from the house. It was a man I assumed was her father. When he got into the car and drove off, it spurred me into keeping my promise to Dinky. I approached the door and gave the heavy brass knocker three, sharp, determined raps.

Mrs Evans was a large woman, with thinning red hair and a rounded face. Her breasts were enormous. Harry always said they resembled two rugby balls. Above all else she was known in the district for her voice. It was very loud and she was extremely proud of it. She was a fastidious churchgoer, attending St John's twice every Sunday for the morning and evening services. Taking up a commanding position in the centre pews, she would treat both the congregation and the surrounding district to her booming tones. She stood out as the remainder of the congregation always gave her plenty of space. When she opened the door and looked down at me squirming, her manner was brusque.

"What do you want Handel?" she said in a deep voice.

She had a bossy manner and little time for boys – particularly former choirboys like me.

"Oh, 'ello Mrs Evans. I'm looking for Dinky – is 'e in your 'ouse?" I blurted out in blind panic.

At the time it seemed to be the only safe thing to say as I was too scared to mention Biddy. I knew as soon as I finished speaking that I was wrong. If anyone would know where Dinky was it would have been me, but it was too late. The damage was done. She fixed me with an accusing, piercing look and her eyes narrowed.

"You of all people, Handel Swain, should know very well where

Dinky is. I don't know what your game is. Now clear off and don't come back."

I retreated from Odo Street as quickly as I could. Dinky's message of love had, it seemed, very little chance now of being delivered to Biddy.

I went back to the square and sat on our garden wall. It was a typical, lazy summer's day. The Hafod was generally quiet after dinner on Saturdays. It was a half-day for most working people. Many of the women would head into Swansea – to the shops and most of the men would be in the pubs where they would stay until chucking out time at three o'clock.

As I sat on the wall in the sunshine I began to daydream. It was becoming an increasingly regular habit as I sought solace in a make-believe world. Often I would dream of going down the prom and meeting Iris. She would rush to my arms embracing and kissing me as we did in our brief courtship. I relived this again and again. Then I would think of Erica. Although I made regular visits to our 'secret place' I hadn't seen her for two years.

It was at this point that I had an overwhelming desire to climb that rock face again and visit what really was a special place. Normally I would head straight for the council refuse dump and the quarry, but instead I decided to visit Llewellyn Park first. Its wide expanse of grass, the pond and the small wood with its unusual trees never failed to impress me. This was a longer route to the quarry, but it meant I could avoid passing the cemetery where the road was shaded by the tall trees.

The park was busy. Some small children watched by a few adults played in and around the pond. Generally I would skirt around this, cross the patch of rough grassland before heading back down to the river. Instead I found myself wandering past the sloping football field where some youths were having a kick-around. From there I carried on towards the double tennis courts. Both were occupied by young men and women smartly turned out in tennis whites. That was a game I didn't understand and had no wish to. To me it was for posh people.

I wasn't really looking at the tennis players, but one young woman caught my eye – it was Erica! I couldn't believe it. The sight of her springing around the tennis court – as self assured and confident as ever – stunned me. She was taller now and her once gangly body had filled out a little. Gone was the short, boyish haircut. Her long dark hair was now tied back in a pony tail. Partnering her on the court was an equally accomplished sixteen or seventeen year old youth. He was tall, like Erica, with an athletic physique and had slicked-back fair hair plastered with Brylcream. They and their opponents appeared to be completely wrapped up in both the game and themselves with a lot of banter and laughter going on. They were oblivious to my presence and for that I was glad. As I looked down at my boots and baggy grey trousers and compared my shabby appearance to that of Erica and her friends, I quickened my pace and hurried towards the bowling green desperate to erase any thought of her from my mind.

Just like the tennis courts, every rink there was busy as there was a match underway. Normally I would have stayed for a while to watch, but I couldn't forget the image of Erica who appeared so mature and grown up, so different to the quirky girl that I once new. I was angry with her. It would have been better had I never seen her again – ever. I felt that another of my dreams had been shattered.

Llewellyn Park lost a bit of its magic that day. I didn't make it to the quarry or the special place. I would never forget it though, it meant too much to me. Climbing the rock-face, jumping and clinging on to the tree, then scrambling to the top and then the view over the town and the sea was a challenge and a pleasure too hard to relinquish. For three years I had visited the place on my own. It was my special place now and I vowed then that I would never share it with anyone.

I arrived home just in time to collect Walter and Eddie before walking the mile or so to Maggie's for our weekly Saturday evening treat. I was hoping for something special this week as I sorely needed cheering up. I was not to be disappointed. As well as the meat and fish paste sandwiches, jelly and blancmange, Maggie had made some stick-jaw toffee which she wrapped in greaseproof paper for us to take home. As soon as Maggie and Sam had gone back into their house after waving goodbye to us, the toffee was shared out and crammed into our mouths. We arrived home, all mucky and sticky, to a scolding from Mam and ready for our regular Saturday night baths.

CHAPTER 28

Tommy's tasty teatime treat

In the week that followed Biddy's arrival I walked past Mrs Gwen Evans's house several times a day, desperately hoping to catch sight of her elusive grand-daughter. She was only staying for one week and on Saturday her father would be coming to take her home again. My mission had become a personal one now and not just a question of delivering Dinky's message of love. I resented her aunt's rude attitude towards me so I was determined more than ever to set eyes on, and speak to, Biddy. But by the Thursday, with one full day remaining, I still hadn't seen her. I did however see Tommy Thomas.

Surprisingly Tommy had called at our house on Wednesday on his way home from the docks where he was helping his uncle, the man who had supplied the shrimps and cockles for our disastrous seawater aquarium venture. He worked on one of the small trawlers that operated from the South dock and Tommy, who had spent most of the summer holidays at sea, was hoping for a full time job with him when he left school at Christmas.

"Do you want some fish 'andel," he asked.

"Big fish – sea bream they are. Nobody wants 'em mun."

We were standing by the door just inside the kitchen. Mam was at the table cutting bread for tea with the impatient and hungry audience of Walter and Eddie. As alert as ever her antenna had picked up the

195

offer of some free fish and in a flash, before I had taken in what Tommy had said, she was giving him his answer.

"Of course we'll have some boy – have you got them now?" she said, eager to get her hands on this free food source.

"No, Mrs Swain," he answered.

"Tomorrow mun – in the morning – down the docks. Your 'andel must fetch a big bag with 'im mind."

"Don't you worry Tommy boy, he'll be there," she replied and then, as if to make sure we got the fish, she added "What time, Tommy? When should Handel come?"

He was half way through the door now, his stomach telling him to go home for his tea.

"Come early 'andel."

"Yeah, but what time is early mun?" I shouted, running after him.

All I got as he disappeared round the corner of the house was.

"Early – when you get up mun."

To me that meant when he got up which would be about six o'clock in the morning, the normal start time for dockworkers and fishermen. I didn't fancy that one bit so I asked Mam to call me at seven and planned to be on my way ten minutes later.

Most of the mill and factory workers were already attending to their duties by the time I set off the following morning carrying Mam's great shopping bag, the one crafted from the salvaged skin of a barrage balloon. I had to walk down to the docks, but Mam had given me a penny to catch the bus home if the fish were plentiful and the bag was heavy.

I had plenty of company with many tradesmen and shop workers starting work at eight o'clock. I marched along with them through the Hafod, then down into The Strand and on towards the South Dock. This was the busiest time of the day at the docks with the fish market in full swing handling the catches from the larger trawlers that fished the Irish Sea.

I had to pick my way carefully around the quay as the big baskets and boxes of fish were being moved. Inside the market knives and blades were flashing everywhere as the men, working on rows of trestle tables, cleaned and gutted the freshly unloaded fish. I stopped briefly at one point and watched with fascination as one man quickly and methodically skinned some dogfish. Neatly, he slit the skin around the fish's neck before placing his foot on its head and swiftly peeling it away.

The Celtic Waves, the small trawler on which Tommy and his uncle worked, was moored at one side of the dock basin away from the fish market having landed its catch the day before. It would be setting out again on the next tide which was about midday. They wouldn't stay at sea for as long as the bigger trawlers – two or three days at most – but they didn't spend much time ashore either. They had only finished from their last trip late the previous afternoon and here they were preparing to go to sea again. Tommy was waiting for me, standing in the bow of the vessel waving his arms and shouting.

"Come on mun 'andel – you're late boy," he hollered

He had most likely been there since seven o'clock and was demonstrating that he was now in the grown-up world, working alongside men in what was a most dangerous occupation. Tommy loved the sea and he would be proud to call himself a trawlerman. He couldn't wait for Christmas and the time when he could leave school and work full-time on the boat.

"I'm not cowin' daft like you mun," I shouted back.

"You'll be lookin' like a cowin' fish soon. And smellin' like one."

We were both laughing as I approached the boat and he grabbed my hand and pulled me aboard.

"You're a cowin' card you are 'andel," he said grinning. "Come on – I'll show you around."

It was a two men and a boy kind of boat. The men being Tommy's uncle and the skipper, but they hadn't arrived yet. He took me to the cabin where the skipper lived, worked and slept before showing me the incredibly small cubicle in the bow where he and his uncle slept.

"When we have the time," he emphasised.

He showed me the equipment and the winding gear and demonstrated the great importance of inspecting the nets and repairing any holes. Finally he led me to a large basket on the deck which held four huge fish, each one at least a foot and a half long.

"There you are 'andel boy – I kept 'em for your mother. Sea bream they're called and good they are too."

I just stared at them. They looked heavy and a thought was crossing my mind – would I be able to carry them. They posed no problem for Tommy however as he grabbed each fish and rammed them into the bag head first with the tails sticking out of the top. He had just finished when two men came on board. I recognised one – his uncle.

"Come on Tommy, let's get moving," he shouted sternly.

I could tell by his tone that it was a signal for me to get off the boat.

Tommy responded to his order by quickly yanking the bag off the deck and in seconds it was on the quay with me behind. He was already back on deck when he shouted a farewell.

"So long 'andel see you in school next week."

Then as an afterthought he added "My mam stuffs the fish with sage and onion and bakes 'em in the oven."

Quickly he ran to join his uncle who was already busy pulling on some ropes at the stern of the trawler.

Carrying the bag of fish was a two handed job. Taking a rest at intervals every few minutes was essential. Still I had all day and it would be reward enough when I eventually arrived back home with this bonanza of free fish for Mam and the family.

Things were easing up as I retraced my steps past the fish market which was now clear of most of the baskets and boxes. I stopped here and took my first rest in the shade of one of the large trawlers. Unlike Tommy's boat this one had a proper gangway leading from the deck down to the quayside. I noticed that waiting at the bottom was a middle-aged woman, a younger woman and a girl of nine or ten. She could, I thought, be exceptionally pretty, dressed in a smart velvet collared coat with white socks and red buckled shoes. Her blonde hair was held in ringlets tied with a white silk ribbon. For the moment however her little face was blighted by the most enormous pout, one that even my brother Walter would have envied.

I smiled when she briefly glanced at me, but her response was a firming of the pout before she turned her back on me. Obviously she was upset, but a face like that I knew usually indicated someone was not getting their own way. Then as I was about to continue my journey a huge barrel-chested man wearing a heavy seaman's black jacket and a peaked cap emerged from the vessel.

"So long Skipper," someone shouted from inside as he hurried down the gangway.

Immediately the little girl swung around to face him and miraculously the pout disappeared. Instantly she was transformed into a little angel. The older woman took hold of her hand to restrain her until the man cleared the gangway, then swinging her up he hugged her closely in his bear-like arms before they all hurried away. I guessed she must have been the man's daughter and I wondered whether I would ever see her again.

I struggled on out of the docks, across the swing bridge and exhausted, finally arrived at the bus stop in Victoria Road, opposite Swansea Museum. I was just getting my breath back when a dark blue saloon car driven by the younger woman I had seen at the docks swished past. The little girl with the pout was beside her sitting on her father's lap.

I hadn't expected to see her again this soon. She looked directly at me and I smiled at her, but all that the little beggar did in return was to stick her tongue out at me.

I was certainly glad that Mam had given me a penny for the bus ride home as those fish were really heavy and I don't think I could have walked much further with them. Mam was delighted with the fish and remembering Tommy's words I repeated them to her.

"Tommy says his Mam stuffs 'em with sage and onions – and bakes 'em in the oven."

She did the same and they were a treat too. There was a sumptuous feast in the Swain household that night with Maggie and Sam, Molly and Sid, all in attendance.

Mam said that she found it hard to understand that wholesome fish like the bream had failed to find a market, especially with good food being so hard to get hold of.

CHAPTER 29

Falling head over heels for Biddy

The last weekend of the school summer holidays proved a hectic time for Mam, even though there were only three of us left in school. It seemed she was faced with an endless list of things to do before Monday morning arrived. I was happy to help ease her load by running errands and fetching bread, vegetables and other groceries, but there was one task I hated – going to the cobblers over by Hafod bridge to collect footwear that had been left for repair.

On this occasion my quest was to collect an old pair of Harry's boots Mam had left there to have some work done on them. I was to have this pair and my boots in turn were to be passed down to Eddie. Although he was younger than Walter he had outgrown him and so was next in line for my hand-me-downs.

I hated going to the cobblers for a number of reasons. There was always a queue there or someone turning up when his boots or shoes weren't ready or someone who needed a small repair, pressing the cobbler to deal with them first by whinging that they had nothing else to wear. Grown-ups wouldn't tolerate this, but a young boy could be ignored and true to form that is exactly what happened.

I queued for half an hour only to be told that my boots weren't ready and I would have to come back after dinner. So just before two o'clock I was there again – in a queue – behind three other people. It was around three o'clock when I set off back home again. I decided to go up the Cwm along one of the many paths carved by a generation of children going to and from the park there. The chain link fencing that once formed the boundary had been allowed to decay and was now almost completely torn down and flattened underfoot.

The park was always popular with children, especially the playground with its swings and roundabouts and this day was no exception. Some young children accompanied by their mothers, were enjoying the swings while two older girls were winding up the jerker to which a group of older children clung on screaming in delight. There were also two roundabouts, one at low level with wooden boards and the other, the spider's web, constructed entirely of metal beams revolving on a centre post about three feet high. It was an apparatus that only the brave and daring would tackle when it was going full pelt.

Suddenly I noticed that there, perched on the outer rail of the spider's web, was the elusive Biddy Roberts. I took a second look to confirm my observation. I was delighted, until I spotted someone else sitting on a park bench. No more than six feet away was her grandmother. While still not believing my luck, I carried on walking, keeping my head down, not daring to look directly at them for fear of being scolded again by the old woman.

Although I had not seen Biddy for well over a year there was no doubt that it was her. She was never allowed out on her own, even Dinky only knew her from the rare occasions when he was invited into her grandmother's house to play with her. From my brief glance I noticed that she had grown considerably. Her once bob-cut black hairstyle had been replaced by shoulder length locks held in place by an emerald green ribbon. She was dressed in a tight fitting, light blue frock emphasising the curves of her developing figure. I could hardly believe that she was only thirteen.

My head was filled with mixed emotions as I hurried home across the football field. I felt strangely enthralled by the unexpected appearance of this girl. Our eyes had not met, yet I felt entirely captivated by her presence. I refused to think that I would never see her again although the odds of this happening were not in my favour, particularly if Mrs Gwen Evans had a hand in things.

Luckily Mam had no further errands for me to run when I got back home, but she did insist that I try out the boots I had brought back from the cobbler's to ensure that they were fit for me to wear to school the following Monday. They were a bit tight and felt strange as hobnails, which were rapidly going out of fashion, had not been included in the repairs. She suggested that I kept them on to start wearing them in. I didn't object as I only had one thought in my head and that was Biddy.

I returned to the park, wincing on the way from pain to the toes on my right foot and hobbling slightly. I should have expected it I know, but by the time I returned to the playground Biddy and her grandmother were gone. It was only as I jumped onto the spider's web, that I realised I hadn't been in the park for almost a year. All the equipment there was painted in dark green and that was probably why, when I first got on the spider's web, I hadn't noticed Biddy's emerald green ribbon tied to one of the steel rods near its centre. It was wishful thinking perhaps, but I came to the conclusion that I hadn't seen the last of Biddy Roberts.

My first thought as I untied the ribbon and held it in my hand was that she had spotted me earlier and left it as a keepsake for me until we met again. On the other hand perhaps she wanted me to take it to her grandmother's house as an excuse to see her? I didn't fancy that option as it would have meant coming face to face with Mrs Gwen Evans again which was a dreadful thought.

I was pushing my feet against the ground, slowly turning the spider's web and lapsing into a daydream. I had a growing desire to see Biddy again. I imagined that somehow she intended to escape from her grandmother's clutches by using the retrieval of the ribbon as an excuse to return to the park. It would not take a great effort on her part to show her gran just how distressed she was at losing it.

My thoughts turned to what I would say if she turned up. Would I carry out my original promise and deliver Dinky's message – that he had chosen her for his girlfriend. This would not be an easy task especially as I was convinced that he hadn't made any effort to tell her himself. As for the alleged threat from Brammer of stealing a march on him with Biddy while he was away, well that had clearly not materialised. My head was spinning with all these mixed up thoughts as the roundabout lazily continued to rotate when suddenly the soft tones of a young female voice stirred me from my daydreams.

" Hello Handull," it murmered.

I spun around to discover the unimaginable. There, sitting beside me, was Biddy. She was smiling and swinging her legs as she took the ribbon from my hand. Then, shaking her head to show off her long black hair she tied it neatly in place.

"Thank you for finding my ribbon Handull," she said, before coyly announcing, "I had no idea just where I had lost it."

She shook her hair once more, running her fingers through it and adjusting the ribbon.

"Oh I missed it so much I even cried to Nana Evans to let me come and look for it," she said. "Shame that she was so tired she couldn't come and help. So aren't I lucky Handull that I've got you to come to my rescue."

My brief courtship with Iris and experience with Erica had taught me that girls have far greater imaginations than boys and can tell fibs so very convincingly. Still I didn't care what she had told her 'Nana' as she referred to the formidable Mrs Gwen Evans. I was just so glad that she was sitting on the spider's web alongside me. I liked the way she talked, her voice soft and mellow, its slight Shropshire accent apparent only when she pronounced my name. 'Handull' she would say, drawing out the end. Nevertheless I still felt a little intimidated by her. She was very pretty and looked older than I expected. I wanted to impress her but I was unsure of what to say, so I reverted to what most boys would probably do under these circumstances. Where words may fail – actions prevail.

Without warning I started running full pelt, pushing the spider's web as fast as it would go. I wasn't sure whether she was screaming out of sheer delight or fear. Either way her air of confidence vanished as she desperately clung on to the roundabout. I continued racing round and round before I finally jumped on beside her. I felt triumphant and full of confidence as we kept spinning to her cries of "Stop! Stop! Stop!" and then "Oh Handull, slow it down, please slow it down."

Of course I was going to do no such thing. Being full of bravado I decided to impress her further. Letting out a jungle-piercing Tarzan cry, I took a flying leap from the spider's web intending to land on the run as I had done on countless previous occasions. It was a big mistake. I had not taken the stiff soles on my newly repaired boots, or the absence of hobnails into account. As a result I hit the ground with my right foot leading and that's the way I remained. I went into a long slide, stopping only when my left knee hit the ground, throwing my body forward and causing me to bounce a couple of times on the tarmac before finally ending up sprawled out, face down. Biddy was still screaming as I struggled to sit up from my disastrous landing. Then to add insult to injury, one of the youngsters who had been playing on the swings ran to her rescue. He dug his heels into the ground and with a struggle brought the spider's web to a halt.

Biddy finally stopped screaming as she slowly clambered off the now stationary web. I could see she was out of breath and unsteady on her feet. Her legs were wobbling as she slowly made her way over to me, with the little lad who had halted the spider's web following closely behind her.

"Are you alright Handull?" she asked in her soft voice.

I was expecting her to be furious with me after my daft act of bravado, yet here she was probably feeling giddy herself but showing genuine concern.

Initially I was determined to put on a brave face, but I quickly realised that I would be better off with a demonstration that I was seriously injured. Gripping my left knee which was in fact very painful, I screwed up my face, winced and sucked in air for effect.

"Oh Biddy – my leg mun – I think I've broken my leg," I moaned.

She knelt down at my side and put her arm around my shoulder.

"Don't move Handull, rest a moment I'm sure you'll be alright in a minute," she said soothingly.

To my horror the little boy who seemed to have grown quite attached to Biddy was having none of this. He was behind me, his fingers digging into my ribs.

"Come on mun don't be a baby – rub your leg and get up," he taunted cheekily.

Obviously he was simply repeating advice given to him by his parents when he had taken a knock. It was something I would indeed have done under normal circumstances, but not then, not when I was seeking solace from Biddy. As it happened his words just spurred her into action. She could see where my injury was as I was still grasping my left leg with an exaggerated look of anguish on my face. Then to my amazement she began tenderly massaging my knee. Whether it was doing my knee any good I don't know but I certainly felt that I

205

wanted her to continue as the pained look on my face gradually changed to one of rapture and relief.

"Does that feel better Handull?" she asked.

"Oh yes Biddy" I replied. "That's making me feel a lot better."

At which the little lad who seemed to want to run the show piped up once again.

"That's right, rub it some more mun, that's what my Mammy does when I'm 'urt." Then he began tugging at my arm and spluttering.

"You should get up too, mun."

He was a bossy little devil and I wished that he would just go away, but Biddy seemed to think that his words were sound advice.

"Yes Handull, come on try to stand up," she said taking hold of my other arm and emulating the boy, by pulling at it. I was soon yanked to my feet. Biddy continued to hold on to me putting her arm protectively around my shoulder. But the little know-all wasn't finished yet. He let go of my arm and started demonstrating what I should do next.

"Do this mun. Do this. To get the blood going," he exclaimed as he theatrically stamped his foot onto the ground.

I realised of course that he was still meticulously carrying out his mother's instructions, convinced that I wouldn't get better until I had completed the full course. So to please him and, hopefully, get rid of him I copied his foot stamping demonstration.

I am ashamed to admit I was sorely tempted to 'accidentally' stamp on him too, in the process, but I thought better of it as I was sure that Biddy – who was now holding on to me ever so tightly – would not approve if I hurt her little hero. Mercifully we were spared any further advice on how to get better after a fall when the other lad who had been playing with him started walking away from the playground.

"Oy! Willie, where you goin' mun?" he shouted after him.

"I'm going 'ome," the smaller boy, probably his younger brother, replied. Our little know-all who had most likely been told to look after his younger brother by his mother didn't hesitate. He knew where his duty lay and shrugging his shoulders he ran after his brother. With a final disapproving glance at Biddy and me as if to say 'you'll have to look after yourselves now' he disappeared.

Still cradling me, Biddy took hold of my arm and placing it around her shoulder, helped me as I limped towards the park bench that Mrs

Gwen Evans had occupied only an hour before. Then, with our arms around each other, we sat down. Biddy was a forthright young girl and tactile too as I quickly discovered. Tightening her grip on my shoulder she asked a question that I should have been prepared for, but wasn't. "Why are you chasing after me Handull?" she said softly.

Her remark that I was 'chasing after her' surprised me. I was lost for words, my brain and tongue locked in a state of paralysis as I struggled to find a suitable reply. Before today I had never even spoken to her. I had just caught the odd glance of her over the many years she had visited her grandmother. I knew nothing about her really, only what I had been told by Dinky, so I just blurted out the first thing that came into my head.

"It was Dinky – he asked me to see you," I said nervously.

When I mentioned Dinky she gave a shriek of surprised laughter.

"Little Dinky – what does he want?" she exclaimed.

Having already decided that I was not going pass on his message, especially now we were sitting with our arms locked around one another I had no option but to lie to her.

"Only to play with you," I stuttered, before adding "As 'e is away on holiday 'e said you might want someone to play with."

My face reddened giving the game away that I had told a lie. And she knew it too. She laughed again, shaking her head in a sort of mocking fashion.

"I don't believe that one bit Handull," she said teasingly. Then, coming even closer to me, her face almost touching mine, her dark brown eyes half closed, she whispered, "You are chasing after me Handull – I know you are."

From my first and only experience of kissing a girl – Iris – I at least had some idea now of what I should do when a girl got this close and had that look in her eyes. I was still a little hesitant, but I did move my head in the right direction. Then, copying her, I half closed my eyes until eventually my lips touched hers.

What followed next can only be described as breathtaking. Our lips met and in an instant she was no longer sat beside me, but instead had snuggled up on my lap. One of her arms was cradling my neck while the other snaked around my waist. Her lips were half open and moist, her breath warm on my face, as we embarked on an almost ferocious entanglement of arms and legs as our passion increased. Then somehow – they say that love will find a way – she was on top of me as we laid ourselves down on the park bench. Many years were to pass before I experienced such passion as I encountered that day.

There was probably only one voice in the whole of Swansea that would have been capable of breaking the intense clinch we were locked in – that of Mrs Gwen Evans.

And without any warning, like an unexpected gun shot, that is exactly what blasted through the still, silent air of the park.

"Biddy Roberts! Biddy Roberts! Get up here at once!" she ordered her granddaughter. The shock to our senses was so great that we sprung apart instantly. I ended up on the ground while Biddy scrambled off the bench and flew up the slope to her furious grandmother. The pain from the knock to my knee along with that of my tight fitting, newly-repaired boots had miraculously disappeared during my entanglement with Biddy, but it returned with a vengeance as I made my way home.

The day which began with a visit to the hated cobbler's had ended, lovingly, if only briefly in the arms of Biddy Roberts. It seemed she was anything but the sweet and demure young thing that Dinky was smitten by and whose love he was prepared to die for. I didn't feel the least bit guilty for what happened, I had not set out to seduce her; if anything the reverse was true.

When Dinky eventually returned from holiday and inevitably asked what happened I just told him that Mrs Gwen Evans wouldn't let me see Biddy. I also assured him I did keep an eye on her and that Brammer – who he regarded as his great rival – was never to be seen. That of course was true. What I didn't say however was that there was a third suitor in the frame now – me.

Until my encounter with Biddy Roberts, my limited experience of girls – with Iris and Erica – my thoughts and feelings about them were drawn purely from a tale of old fashioned romance. Biddy however was straight out of the exploits of Hank Jansen.

Even though Dinky was my best pal I decided that there was no way that I would give her up. When it came to chasing after Biddy it was now a case of every man for himself.

CHAPTER 30

Tragedy mixed with triumph

When September 1950 arrived it brought with it a landmark in my education and my life – the beginning of my final year in school. It wasn't to be a complete year, just two terms, as I would be fifteen in January and as a result would be able to leave school at Easter. Overseeing this auspicious period of my schooldays was a new headmaster – Mr Williams – as the mighty Joe Morgan had moved on to become headmaster of Townhill School. Although lacking his predecessor's presence, Mr Williams still carried with him the air of a wise old professor. He was tall and slim with a pallid complexion and a full head of long, grey hair.

I was now in J4, a class in the charge of Mr Summers, a portly, middle-aged man with ruddy features and receding hair. At first he appeared to be an austere, rather reserved character, but we soon discovered he was a no-nonsense teacher excellent at getting his message across. Under his guidance I was delighted to discover that after we had completed the assessment exams at the beginning of the school year I came top of the class.

At any time this was an achievement to be proud of, but being number one in the school's most senior class brought with it the enviable position of being appointed as the headmaster's special monitor. It was a task of great responsibility and trust and I must admit

I felt extremely proud to be the chosen one. I know that Mam and the rest of my family felt particularly proud of this achievement too.

My duties as headmaster's monitor were many and varied. They included running errands for him, helping out in the school stockroom, guiding visitors to his study and one activity of which he could be extremely proud – helping him to teach children to tell the time.

Whenever the headmaster needed my assistance he would summon me by tapping the radiator pipe in his room which was directly under my classroom. Immediately I would stop whatever I was doing and, without needing to ask the teacher's permission, hurry to his study.

Being the headmaster's monitor proved to be invaluable as it kept me busy and gave me something to occupy my mind. The final school year was a strange and difficult time for both the teacher and the boys. At the start of the first term in September the class would be full but after Easter the following year the number of boys would be reduced by up to two thirds. Many of the pupils seemed to lose any interest they might have had in their schoolwork. They probably felt that there was nothing further for them to gain, especially those leaving at the end of a particular term. All of their time, effort and thought would be concentrated on one thing only – getting a job. As for Mr Summers I believe he saw his main task as one centred on trying to round off the boys' skills, particularly if they were found to be lacking in subjects like reading and writing, in an attempt to prepare them for adult life.

All of this however, was punctuated definitively by a tragic event that shocked the whole of Swansea and South West Wales just at a time when people were beginning to pick themselves up after the horrors inflicted during the Second World War.

Just as we were settling down to another year of school life and getting used to days of routine following our holiday relaxation, the area suffered its worst tragedy and loss of life since the Three Nights' Blitz of February 1941. It was an incident that happened without any warning in the early hours of Saturday, September 9. Three houses in Prince of Wales Road collapsed, sadly resulting in the deaths of seven people including five children. Many more people were injured as the houses which were built over huge arches slid, in an avalanche of rubble, into The Strand below. These arches were occupied by the businesses of a number of rag and bone and scrap metal merchants, places where I and many children like me in the Hafod had often taken empty jars, bottles and the occasional bag of rags to be exchanged for a few pennies.

News of the disaster spread through the town like wildfire and within hours a huge crowd including myself had gathered in The Strand, watching scores of rescue workers battling to remove the debris in a desperate search for survivors. Most of the dead and injured were recovered quickly and by late afternoon only one man was unaccounted for. Strangely I can't recall being accompanied by anyone else but I did visit the scene of devastation several times during that day. The last time was in the early evening but the man was still missing. Sadly I learned the following day that he too had died and that his body had been recovered late in the night. The news made headlines in all of the local newspapers including the Evening Post. The incident was one of the biggest peacetime tragedies our town had experienced.

It was a cruel blow to those families who suffered, particularly coming as it did after they had endured the hardship and terror of the Second World War just a few years before.

The following Monday morning prayers were said in the school assembly for the dead and injured, especially the children. People of the town remained in a state of some shock for a long time afterwards often comparing the tragedy to episodes during the wartime blitz.

Many people seemed to harbour a great bitterness about the incident. It was almost as though it had far greater impact than the war itself. During the war we knew who the enemy was – the German Luftwaffe. They attacked us from the air, but we expected that and were prepared for the consequences. If nothing else we could vent our feelings, swear vengeance upon them and wait for the time when we could strike back. The Prince of Wales Road incident however, was different. It was almost as though the pain had been self-inflicted. What was particularly tragic was that it came at a time when the first stirrings of hope of better things to come were beginning to appear in peoples' hearts and minds.

Swansea continued to grieve for some time after the fatal tragedy that had killed and injured so many in what after all was peace time. But life had to go on. And in the Swain household it was necessary to focus on a singular event that would mark a time of jubilation for the family. The big event was the wedding of Molly and Sid. They were to be married on Boxing Day, so we were in line for a far different Christmas with the two celebrations going hand in hand.

The preparations for the wedding seemed to take precedence over those for the festive season. The duty of giving the bride away once again fell to Daniel. He had already risen to the challenge of a similar role the year before, when Maggie got married. He was still in the Army and had fortunately remained in the United Kingdom, having avoided being sent to any of the world's troubled areas, especially war-torn Korea.

The preparations seemed to be going smoothly enough until late November, just a month before the wedding when disaster struck – Molly couldn't find red shoes to match the red handbag she had bought to go with her cream going away outfit. She had searched Swansea, even enlisting the help of friends and family, but had failed to find any. Everyone agreed that there was only one option – a shopping trip to Cardiff!

Things were looking up for Sid since he had landed a new job as a bus conductor. He had even acquired his own transport, a motorcycle and sidecar or combination as it was known by the motoring minded. It was a Norton Dominator, a powerful machine, which was just as well as it needed all of its 1000cc power to pull the huge box of a sidecar. This was about four foot long and two foot wide and to me it resembled a miniature coffin on wheels. There wasn't even a windscreen to protect the passenger. But Sid convinced us all, particularly Mam who had a phobia for motorcycles and their safety, that it was sound. He had after all been riding motorcycles in the Army. The day of reckoning finally arrived. The very first trip of any distance for the combination was to convey Molly to Cardiff on her desperate quest for the elusive red shoes. Sid had a day off and Molly too must have been excused Saturday morning duties by her employers. The epic journey was planned to cover the forty miles or so from Swansea to Cardiff along the main A48 road.

With Molly riding in the side-car there was space on the pillion, behind Sid, for an extra passenger. Molly decided that the opportunity should not be wasted and I was given the dubious honour of accompanying them. Off we went one bright and breezy Saturday morning, leaving Hafod Square about ten o'clock with all of our family and most of the neighbours there to see us off. Mam had insisted that Molly and I were well wrapped up against the elements. Sid had managed to get some oilskins, fishermen's hats and goggles too, for him and Molly. He also provided protective clothing for me.

Luckily Sid was on the small side and said his double-breasted waterproof raincoat fitted me a treat, though when I put it on it reached down to my ankles. I didn't need goggles, he added, but my head needed covering and for this he had borrowed an old Jackie Coogan cap, the brim of which rested on my ears and eyebrows. I must have looked a sight as I marched out of the house that day to join Molly and Sid on the motorcycle. Thankfully Harry was in work otherwise he would have subjected me to some cruel teasing, but I didn't escape altogether. Our neighbour, Mr Davies, couldn't resist pulling my leg.

"It's a good job Guy Fawke's night has gone Handel or they'd be chucking you on the bonfire," he shouted with a laugh.

The route to Cardiff took us along Neath Road to Morriston. After this I was in uncharted territory but the much-travelled Sid knew his way. As we headed through Neath the first specks of rain began to fall. It was a bit trickier and time-consuming negotiating Port Talbot which was very congested. From here, as we headed for Bridgend, the rain became more persistent and the wind increased. Soon we were travelling along in a torrential downpour. I was glad when at last, windswept and bedraggled, we arrived in Cardiff.

Sid pulled into the railway station car park as we were to have our dinner at the prestigious Red Dragon Buffet, which I imagined must have been named after the crack Paddington to Swansea express. It appeared to be very classy, so perhaps it wasn't surprising that we were greeted with some odd looks from the other diners when we presented ourselves to the head waiter and asked for a table for three.

Sid and Molly looked like two distressed fishermen while I resembled a sodden scarecrow. Fortunately for us, true professional that he was, the head waiter greeted us with courtesy and directed us to the cloakroom so we could remove our soaking outer garments.

Five minutes later – Molly needed that amount of time in front of the mirror after being exposed to the elements – he guided us to our table. For a fourteen-year-old boy from the Hafod, dining in a place like this, with its bright chandeliers, crisp white cloths and men in suits, felt like being in the movies. The three course set menu consisted of minestrone soup, braised steak and vegetables and apple tart with

213

custard. Sid had provided us with a memorable meal and by the time we had finished, we felt ready to face the world once more as we emerged from the restaurant to continue with our primary reason for visiting the metropolis – our quest for Molly's elusive red shoes. Fortunately the rain had stopped and there was even a hint of sunshine. Sid had no qualms about stashing the oilskins into the sidecar which he left in the station car park, but he didn't want to lose his best double-breasted raincoat so he decided that I should keep it on, but I didn't have to wear the Jackie Coogan cap.

My first impression of Cardiff as we made our way across Wood Street from the railway station was how dense and crowded the city appeared compared to Swansea. Unlike my home town, its city centre hadn't suffered so badly from wartime bombing. The four and five storey buildings in St Mary Street appeared to press down on us and strangely our only avenue of escape was to enter them. I was also amazed by my first sighting of Cardiff's trolley buses quietly swishing along the city's streets. I had never seen anything like them before.

Molly had been told to look out for two shops in particular – David Morgan in The Hayes and James Howells in St Mary Street. For me and for Sid too, though he never showed it, this was the worst part of what was otherwise a very exciting day. I didn't like shopping, probably because I had spent so much of my young life in queues, and these great department stores selling mainly clothes and furniture held no attraction for me. But Molly loved it.

Starting at James Howells she covered virtually every department, particularly those containing the new furniture and kitchen appliances that were just becoming available again after the war. She had expensive taste, showing Sid just how she would like to furnish and equip their home in the future. After that it was on to the clothing departments, first to the men's section for about five minutes where Sid, being a bit of a snappy dresser, momentarily perked up. I think that was an attempt by Molly to keep up his flagging interest as we seemed to spend a lifetime in the ladies dress and gown shop, before we finally arrived at where I thought we were supposed to be in the first place – the shoe department.

There appeared to be more shoes there than feet in the entire world to wear them, with more than enough red ones. So out came Molly's handbag and almost immediately Sid found a pair of matching shoes

214

or so he thought. Molly tut-tutted. "Don't be silly Sid, that's nothing like the colour," she said as she held the shoes up at various angles to reflect the light.

She did this with two or three other pairs, muttering away to herself before finally deciding.

"No. Sid," she said. "None of these are any good. We shall have to go to David Morgan's."

Sid did his best to resist.

"Are you sure mun, Molly," he moaned.

"I thought that first pair was just right."

She didn't say a word. The withering look of disdain she gave him as she marched off was enough to silence him. He just shrugged his shoulders and with a despairing look at me we trudged off after her.

The Hayes, although busy, seemed less crowded than St Mary's Street probably because of its odd shape like a huge, elongated triangle. There were many street traders here with the dominant feature being the David Morgan department store.

Once inside the procedure was reversed. We started in the clothing departments first before going on to the furniture. I was beginning to suspect that Molly might already have seen the shoes she wanted, but needed an excuse to visit this store as well. She was determined that her big day out in Cardiff, or most of it at least, would be spent where it mattered – in the shops.

It was when we were on our way to look at shoes, at long last, that we passed through the electrical department. There seemed to be quite a fuss in one corner where a group of people had gathered. There must have been thirty or forty of them all staring intently at something which at first, I couldn't see. But Sid had and headed over to join the crowd excitedly calling Molly and me to follow him as he went.

"Come on you two – come and look at this," he called.

He barged his way through the crowd with Molly and me behind him until we got closer to the front where I could see what everyone was staring at. I had heard of these contraptions before, but had never seen one – it was a television set. There was no moving picture on the screen, just a photograph of a building which was probably Broadcasting House. The screen was tiny, less than twelve inches square. But the cabinet which housed it was huge, about four feet high and two feet wide. Wisely, which was more than could be said for the rest of us who seemed to be fixed in some sort of trance by this magic box, Molly soon lost interest in looking at what really was just a box with a picture on it and she began to walk away.

"We've come here to look for my shoes – not at that silly thing," she said to Sid.

She felt this was her day and she was not going to play second fiddle to anything, even if it was one of the great inventions of the twentieth century.

Finally we arrived in the shoe department where there was a similar display to that at Howells, the first store we had visited. Incredibly, without hesitation, after a quick scan of the red shoes on display, Molly found the very ones she had been searching for. Out came the handbag again, the shoes were held up to the light before she triumphantly proclaimed "These are the ones Sid – a perfect match. See. I knew that if I persevered long enough I would find the right ones to match my handbag."

Like me I think Sid was a little suspicious that they were the same shoes we had first seen in Howell's store over an hour before. Wisely he kept his thoughts to himself. As for me I was only too glad that at last she had found her matching shoes and we could leave the shops.

It was dark when we eventually left the store and the Hayes appeared gloomy now in the poor street lighting. I really thought that as Molly had found her shoes we would be making our way back to the station, the motorbike and then home, but Molly had other ideas. She was not finished with her day out yet.

Sid had told her that Cardiff was a city of enclosed arcades lined with shops, which she was anxious to visit as we only had one similar place in Swansea which connected High Street with Orchard Street. So we spent the next half an hour ambling around a maze of side streets popping in and out of these arcades with Molly inspecting the wares of the scores of small shops within them.

Mercifully Sid called an end to our torturous tour when we ended up outside a dingy little cinema in one of the back streets. It specialised in Continental films, regarded by some as being rather saucy and racy. A small queue had formed at the entrance as people began to arrive for the evening screening. Sid scrutinised the boards advertising what was on.

"It's a French film Molly," he said as his face lit up and his voice filled with excitement. "And it looks good too. Let's go in, right."

I could see that Molly didn't share his enthusiasm. She had probably heard about these French films. I knew that I had and I was definitely with Sid on this.

"Oh come on mun, Molly," I moaned. "I'm fed up looking in shops an' I'm tired – I want to sit down."

I was her favourite brother and perhaps she felt a little guilty after dragging me around the shops.

"Oh Handel," she said tenderly with a look of pity on her face,
"Do you really – want to see a French film?"

That was enough for Sid. He didn't wait for her to finish speaking. The look on her face confirmed that she agreed, as quickly he ushered us to join the queue. Then he said and did something which I thought was odd. There was an age limit, restricting admission to people over the age of sixteen. People like me.

"Give me your cap Handel," he whispered.

I delved into the pocket of the raincoat, brought out the cap and handed it to him as he furtively looked around before ramming it on to my head, pulling the peak down almost over my eyes.

"Keep it on like that Handel, right. And don't take it off 'til we're inside, right."

As the queue started to move forward I must have looked really odd squeezed between him and Molly. I did get a quick and quizzical look from the lady at the cash desk when Sid was paying for the tickets but she didn't get a second chance as I was whisked rapidly away wedged between him and Molly.

I hadn't given much thought to the fact that the film was French and I know it sounds daft, but it came as a bit of a shock to discover that the actors were speaking in a language I didn't understand. However there were English sub-titles which did help – a little. I don't think the translation was all that good as there was dead silence in the cinema when the characters on the screen were in fits of laughter. I didn't mind though, as going to any cinema was still a treat. And with a bit of effort – trying to watch the film and read the sub-titles – I rather enjoyed it mainly because the plot was so original and the action nothing if not bizarre and saucy.

The story was centred on a small fictional French town called

Clochmerle, also the film's title, between the two world wars in the great wine area of Beaujolais. The story is based on the construction of a pissoire, or urinal and the lives of the people for and against it.

The film brought an unexpected and unusual end to my first visit to Cardiff after which I always associated the place with the fictional French film town of Clochmerle.

CHAPTER 31

Wedding bells, but only just!

A s 1950 drew to a close it seemed that everything was being brushed aside to ensure that plans for Molly and Sid's wedding could proceed unhindered. To me Christmas time seemed an odd time to have a wedding, but my sister and her fiancée were determined that Boxing Day would be the date on which they tied the knot. Daniel was to give the bride away, just as he had done the previous year when Maggie and Sam were married. Maggie had a role to play in this wedding too. Tradition dictated that as she was no longer a single woman she couldn't be a bridesmaid as Molly had been for her. Instead she was accorded the grand title of Maid of Honour. Like Maggie, Molly was to be married at St John's Church with the Rev. Leslie Norman conducting the ceremony.

We did of course celebrate Christmas but not quite with the usual fervour, particularly as far as Mam was concerned. She was hard pressed ensuring that Molly's big day went off as smoothly as possible. One thing that wasn't lacking though was all the usual festive trimmings. Walter and Eddie hung up their stockings which, while they slept, were miraculously filled with apples, oranges, nuts, chocolates and sweets. We also had Mam's delicious cakes and puddings and of course the centrepiece of every Christmas day – the chicken dinner. Mam didn't forget that, even with all the excitement of the wedding these things were important to us as family, especially the younger members. We all received presents and it was mine in particular – the wedding apart – that was the reason I shall always remember Christmas of 1950.

I was given The Story of Living Things and Their Evolution, a book which I treasured from the moment I received it. Documenting the origins of life on earth it was always referred to in the family as Handel's Big Book. There was an explosion of interest at that time in the evolution of life and also the origin of prehistoric animals and creatures. The BBC ran a series of programmes for schools on the subject which fascinated me. I had a strong interest in all things historical and I expect it was a natural progression for this to develop into pre-history. So when this book was advertised in one of the Sunday newspapers I just had to have it. There was one small snag however, the cost. At two pounds ten shillings it was just a little on the expensive side. The publishers offered a way around this though – the book could be purchased on the 'never-never'. They would accept a deposit of ten shillings with the balance to be paid at one shilling a week for forty weeks.

I didn't believe that Mam would go along with this idea but as I was desperate to get my hands on a copy of the book I could only hope for the best when I put my plan to her. The big obstacle I knew was getting the deposit of ten shillings. If she could manage to pay this as my Christmas present – then I would pay off the balance at a shilling a week. I knew it was a lot to ask for and I wasn't surprised that her first reaction was to reject my idea out of hand.

I was determined not to give up in my quest to own this amazing publication however. I knew I had strong allies in Daniel and Molly, but he unfortunately was away in the Army and wouldn't be home in time and Molly was floating on heavenly clouds pending her forthcoming wedding. I was convinced though that she would encourage Sid to help with the deposit. This would in turn prompt Maggie into persuading Sam to chip in too.

It worked. Molly had quite a knack in extracting money from Sid and everything else in my plan fell neatly into place. Mam sent off a ten shilling postal order for the deposit and my Big Book was proudly presented to me, wrapped in some scavenged brown paper on Christmas morning, but before I could begin to turn the pages of my long awaited gift I had a shock. An overnight incident had brought the news that Molly's wedding was off.

Mam in her usual stoic way hadn't said anything. She had just carried on with her busy schedule of preparation for Christmas dinner. I wasn't aware that things hadn't been right between Molly and Sid until mid-morning when Maggie and Sam called to wish us a Merry Christmas. As they approached the house they came across Sid, on his hands and knees, scrabbling about in the front garden paying particular attention to the ground underneath the privet hedge.

Maggie could hardly contain herself when she discovered what he was doing and delivered the news as she burst into the kitchen.

"Have you heard what our Molly's done?" she blurted out.

"She's only gone and thrown her engagement ring at Sid and called off the wedding."

Mam, who was sitting at the table with Walter, Eddie and me and in the throes of peeling the potatoes, simply nodded her head.

"Oh, don't make such a fuss, Mag. It'll blow over shortly – you'll see," came her calm reply.

But Maggie was furious with her sister and demanded to know where she was. She said she wasn't leaving until she had sorted things out and made Molly see sense.

"Where is she then, Mammy," she asked impatiently.

"Still in bed, Mag," Mam replied.

"Came in last night crying and in a temper she was. She said something about Sid dancing with another girl and she didn't want to see him ever again."

Then, in a stern voice, she added "Mind you, she never said anything about throwing the ring at him. I hope it's not lost."

"Well it could be Mammy," said Maggie indignantly.

"That daft lello Sid is outside now looking for it in the bushes. Then she began barking out orders.

"Right! Handel. You, Walter and Eddie, outside now – and help Sid to look for that ring. I'm going to get our Molly to help too, even if I've got to drag her from her bed."

We all knew better than to argue with her and even her husband Sam seemed intimidated by the way she had barked out her orders.

"I'll go and help too, Mag. Right," he piped up.

He was out of the door in a flash with the rest of us on his heels.

Surprisingly when we got outside Sid was sitting on the wall seemingly without a care in the world.

"Hello boys," he said with a broad grin on his face.

"Where's Molly then?"

"Maggie's gone to get her," I replied.

The words had hardly left my mouth when I felt something brush past my shoulder. It was a missile aimed at Sid which smashed right into him almost knocking him off the wall. Now nestling in Sid's lap, it turned out to be one of Molly's shoes and we both realised that there was only one place it could have come from.

I turned and looked up at the front bedroom window and there, with Maggie standing behind her, was Molly.

"Give me back my ring Sid," she shouted.

"I know you've found it. I've been watching you."

I understood then why he was looking so pleased with himself. He had indeed found the ring which he quickly produced from his trouser pocket and began waving, teasingly, at Molly. He believed that he had the upper hand now.

"You come and get it then, my girl," he shouted back with a cocky grin on his face. But she wasn't going to let him off that lightly. He was going to pay for his misdemeanour which we now discovered was that Sid wasn't just dancing with another girl – they were doing the Jitterbug. This was a cardinal sin. He was renowned for his prowess at jitterbugging and Molly believed he should only perform this dance with her. It was like watching a comical version of Romeo and Juliet. Sid stood in the front garden looking up at Molly in the bedroom window. With the wedding arrangements for the following day now at stake they were negotiating terms or rather Molly was laying down the rules. She was generally easy going but she did have a stubborn streak which Sid, like the rest of us, was only too aware of.

Eventually she leaned forward on the window frame and with her blue eyes glaring she pronounced for all to hear "I'm not coming down – 'till you say sorry!"

The exchange of words and recriminations would have gone on all day, but Maggie, not known for her patience, decided that she had heard enough and grabbed Molly firmly by the shoulders.

"Right! I've had enough of this. Downstairs now," she bellowed.

Molly was yanked away from the window and within seconds she was being frog-marched out of the house and thrust into Sid's arms. I think he was shocked by the speed with which Maggie had dealt with the matter as he sat back down on the wall with Molly planted in his lap. Then came the parting shot from Maggie.

"Right Sid! Give the ring back to her now. Kiss and make up. And don't come into the house until you've done so."

The instruction delivered, she turned on her heels and went back inside with the rest of us following.

Finally, after what had seemed like an eternity and the slight hitch the day before – Molly and Sam were married on Boxing Day. The overall timescale seemed much longer than we had endured with Maggie's wedding, probably because Molly involved everyone that she possibly could in helping her with the preparations. She loved all the fuss and being the centre of attention. Maggie on the other hand had just organised everything for her wedding in her own straightforward and efficient way.

Molly and Sid's wedding breakfast was almost identical to that which Mam had laid out for Maggie. Pride of place on the table was a whole, home-cooked, ox tongue. A barrel of beer was delivered with the proviso laid down by Molly that under no circumstances was Sid to be allowed anywhere near it. She hadn't forgotten how he had ended up legless when he took charge of the beer barrel at Maggie's wedding. And I am glad to say that on this occasion Sid conducted himself in an exemplary manner, though this confounded some of the guests including members of his own family, who had expectations of sending him off on his honeymoon in a wheelbarrow. So despite the last minute unexpected hitch of her disagreement with Sid, Molly's wedding went off smoothly and ended on a cheerful and pleasant note.

She looked very smart in her going away outfit, a cream two piece suit with a red handbag and of course the red shoes to match.

CHAPTER 32

Soldier Harry battles it out

The sleeping arrangements in the Swain household were a bit cramped following Molly and Sid's return from their honeymoon. They took over the medium-sized back bedroom which had previously been occupied by Mam and Molly. Mam was moving in with Walter, Eddie and me in the large main bedroom at the front of the house where we had managed to squeeze in two double beds. Harry, meanwhile, continued to sleep on his own in the smaller back bedroom which suited him and everyone else in the house. He and Sid didn't get along very well and it wasn't hard to sense the air of tension and unease whenever they were together in the same room. It was just as well that Harry would be eighteen soon and receiving his call up papers for National Service, but until then he continued to blight our lives with his mood swings.

Unlike the sadness I felt when Daniel went off to join the Army I couldn't wait to see the back of Harry and I am sure, apart from Mam and Maggie, everyone else felt the same way. It seemed strange to me as to just how he and Maggie had become so close as they got older, when I think of all the trouble and pain he had brought upon the family at times – particularly to her. He had finished working as a general dogsbody in the ICI works canteen and was employed as a labourer in the company's warehouse. I must admit that for all his innate belligerence and evil intent he was not work shy. In all those years

that we spent growing up together I cannot recall him ever being absent from work through illness or any other reason.

At about this time Harry developed a keen interest in billiards and snooker which was surprising as he had shown no interest or aptitude at all for sports before. Consequently he spent most of his leisure time during the week at the works social club where they had several billiard and snooker tables. On Friday and Saturday nights however, when he had money in his pockets, he would frequent some of the sleazier pubs in town. Very often he would return from one of these outings showing the signs not only of having drunk too much beer but also of being bruised and battered from fighting. Still I at least was glad of these nocturnal activities. It kept him out of the house and away from the rest of us.

Mercifully we didn't have to wait long for his call-up papers to come. At the end of February 1951, off he marched to join The Royal Artillery. Though it might appear spiteful, if I could have arranged for a band to be playing and flags flying, then I would have. We knew from past experience with Daniel already in the Army that he would be gone for a period of six weeks before we would see him again.

The atmosphere at home became much lighter now that Harry was gone. It seemed like a dark cloud had been lifted from over us. Molly particularly had always felt intimidated by him. She was always uncomfortable in his presence and if she could avoid him, she would. I believe that the sense of fear he generated had increased since Maggie had left and again when Daniel went off to the Army. She had lost the support of two natural allies especially Maggie with her strong and forceful character. She did have Sid now, but I don't think he would have been a match for Harry if it came to a fight. They had settled into married life well and with the departure of Harry the house seemed to come alive with their many friends coming and going.

Sid brought his wind-up gramophone with him when he moved in, filling the house with the swing music of Glen Miller, Tommy Dorsey and Joe Loss. They were always going to parties and dances and at weekends if Sid wasn't working and the weather allowed, they would be off to Mumbles or the Gower bays on the motorcycle combination.

Sometimes on Saturday afternoons I would venture into town and visit the library. As well as borrowing books I had discovered the reference room and enjoyed browsing through the shelves there. If Sid was working and Molly was in town shopping we would meet up at the library then go for a coffee at the Mansel Cafe where they had a juke box.

This was the in thing to do and we'd spend an hour or so listening to all the latest records. It cost threepence for a go on the jukebox and Molly would always pay for a record. After we had listened to it she would catch a bus back home in time to make Sid his tea.

It was after Molly and I had spent one such Saturday afternoon together, that word got back to Sid from one of his workmates on the buses that his wife had been seen cavorting around the town with a young man. We all thought that this was highly amusing and Sid, with his wicked sense of humour, 'confessed' to the informant that he knew all about the affair. He told him that Molly was very close to the young man. She would never give him up and there was nothing that he could do about it!

Towards the end of March, after Harry had been away in the Army for just over a month Mam became very concerned that she had not heard from him. She had written to him at his training camp in North Wales sending a letter every week as she had done with Daniel, but hadn't received a single reply.

Maggie and Molly told her not to worry, that it was just Harry being his usual, thoughtless self. She did feel a little better when they reminded her that he would be coming home soon when he had finished his basic training. But she had also told Daniel about this and he advised her to write to Harry's commanding officer who would in

227

no uncertain terms compel her son to respond to her letters. The Army frowned upon those National Servicemen who upset their mums by failing to write home. Even in his absence it seemed Harry was still causing problems. But there was worse to follow.

Mam duly sent off a letter to Harry's commanding officer and received a reply by return of post. Apparently Harry was in a spot of bother and the CO had not pulled his punches in saying so, a phrase incidentally, which also applied to why he was in trouble.

First of all Harry had been caught smoking on parade which resulted in him being confined to the guardroom for seven days. While he was there he became involved in a fight with members of the Military Police and subsequently ended up in the sick bay. He was currently halfway through serving an additional seven days confinement after which he would be back-tracked to another unit to complete his basic training. In the meantime he would ensure that Harry responded to Mam's letters, but not to expect him home in the near future as he had yet to complete most of his training.

Sure enough within a couple of days Mam received a letter from him – all six lines of it. Basically he said he didn't believe that he had done anything wrong and just couldn't think what all the fuss was about. Naturally Mam was extremely upset by the commanding officer's comments which were only slightly softened when she received a letter from Harry. Anyway, when she replied telling him to behave himself her letter included a note from Maggie which probably put it in stronger terms.

Eventually he did complete his basic training and surprisingly without any further trouble. I could only assume that the military policemen had got the message over to him that they were going to be the only winners if he ever picked a fight with them again.

As luck would have it when he did come home for two weeks, he was on embarkation leave. He was being shipped abroad to Egypt. We wouldn't see him again until he had completed his National Service, a landmark that was almost two years away.

CHAPTER 33

Pride in a job well done

My schooldays were rapidly coming to an end. I was into my final few months in school after which my future was beginning to look anything but certain. The classroom had been severely depleted of pupils on our return from the Christmas holidays. Almost half of my classmates had left at the end of the previous term. Among them was my pal Tommy Thomas. He was lucky. He had landed the job he had always wanted, working with his uncle on the trawler. Mam said that we had been lucky too as Tommy often dropped off the odd fish or two, mostly sea bream or whiting when returning from his fishing trips. For my future employment though, things were looking bleak. I still harboured dreams of following my hero Hank Jansen and becoming an ace reporter. The route to achieving this was by starting as an errand boy in the editorial office of The South Wales Evening Post. Such a job had been advertised in the paper a few times during the period leading up to Christmas, but not since. I could only think, with envy in my heart, that some lucky lad was making a good job of the position and my chance would never come.

There was optimism in the family regarding other work however. Mam believed that there was a good chance of securing a job as a clerk in the offices of ICI. But working as a clerk didn't appeal to me. I let it be known as forcefully as I could that I had no enthusiasm in going down that route. Perhaps in my heart I realised that it was just sheer fancy, some form of escapism from harsh reality, to even think of having aspirations of becoming a journalist.

For a lot of my classmates things were already cut and dried. Whether they liked it or not they were destined to follow in their father's footsteps. This was particularly so if the boy's father worked for one of the public bodies such as the Post Office or the local council or one of the utilities like the gas or electricity boards. These jobs were considered safe and secure and better protected from the scourge of unemployment and the dole queue. It was only natural that fathers would do their utmost to ensure that their sons enjoyed the same benefits and privileges.

The only job that did hold some appeal for me was that of a telegram boy with the Post Office although there was little chance of me getting one. There seemed to be hordes of these riders on the road especially in the town centre where they were always whizzing around on their bikes, wearing smart uniforms with peaked caps, leather belts and wallets which held the telegrams. Dinky I know had grand designs on being a telegram boy, but I thought he would have to grow by at least a foot before his feet could touch the pedals.

With the advent of spring I was still without any prospect of a job and my hopes of starting as an errand boy with the South Wales Evening Post had come to nothing. This was a blow because other than that I had no thoughts about what I wanted to do. It seemed that I was going to drift into a job whether it suited me or not. There was no alternative as I was fifteen and I had to pay my way in life so I had to find some kind of work.

That said, there was no pressure put on me by my family, especially Mam. She had been instrumental in securing Daniel's position by sending him to Gregg's College She had offered me the same chance, but I had turned that down. Harry had also found his job in the copperworks canteen with her help, but thankfully she was aware that a similar job would have been totally unsuitable for me. I always believed that she was confident that I wouldn't fail her. And sure enough fortune smiled on me.

With just days to go before I left school Mr Richards the woodwork teacher thought that he had found a suitable post for me. A local furniture manufacturer had a vacancy for an errand boy with the

230

prospect of becoming an apprentice cabinet maker. They had asked Mr Richards to recommend a lad he thought would be suitable and he offered the chance to me.

Fortunately I had just completed my woodworking project for the term, a small mahogany vanity cabinet with two drawers which I had already presented to Molly as an early birthday present.

"Go home and get that Handel," he said.

"You've done a good job with it. Show them what you can do. The mortice and tenon and dovetail joints on the drawers were excellent. They'll like that Handel. I'm sure you can get that job if you want it."

Up until that moment I had been confused and afraid of committing myself to the wrong job – one which I would hate. But woodwork was a subject which I enjoyed and was reasonably good at, yet I hadn't thought of making a career as a carpenter or cabinet maker. So early on the afternoon of my last day in school, a Friday, I presented myself before the manager of the West Wales Furniture Company and proudly showed off my mahogany vanity cabinet. He appeared to be impressed with my handiwork and to my surprise said that the job was mine. He told me that I could have a week off and then report for work as the company's errand boy at eight o'clock on the first day after the Easter holidays.

I didn't have any great feelings of joy as I dashed back to school to inform Mr Richards that I was successful and to thank him for his help. I was under no illusions that I had been lucky in having his recommendation. Getting a job with the good prospects of learning a trade was not easy to come by. I was grateful for this and of course Mam would be pleased, but I did feel sad that my dreams of aspiring to greater things had not worked out and for the time being at least would have to be abandoned.

Perhaps many other boys had similar feelings – the would-be engine drivers or sailors destined for life as shop assistants or clerks. Even those safe and secure following in the footsteps of their fathers may have had their dreams dashed too.

My spirits were lifted when I arrived back at school just after four o'clock. It wasn't just the end of my school days, it was also the end of term for the whole school and most people had left. I thanked Mr Richards then reported to Mr Summers my teacher who handed me my scholar's leaving card. It was duly completed and signed by

Mr Williams the headmaster. His comments that I was 'honest, intelligent, capable and thoroughly recommended,' gave me an enormous sense of pride.

I was delighted to be thought of in such a way by someone in a responsible and respected position such as his.

CHAPTER 34

Growing strong in a special place

My transition from school life to the world of work was unexpectedly swift and uncompromising, perhaps because I hadn't found a job until my very last day in school. There was just over a week for me to prepare for the day when I started work. Fortunately there was plenty of help and advice on offer from the rest of the family, particularly good old Sid.

He said that having a potential tradesman in the family brought with it particular needs. Top of the list, he said, was the provision of sustenance – food and drink. Mam would provide the food – two lots of sandwiches. One of these would be for my mid-morning break at ten o'clock, which was usually bread and jam, and the other for dinner, of meat, eggs or cheese.

Providing a hot drink – tea – was trickier. For this I needed a billycan – a stout, cone-shaped, enamelled container with a lid that doubled up as a cup. To go with this I would need a caddy for tea and sugar – a small metal container about three inches long, split into two compartments with a lid at either end. Into each compartment went a spoonful of tea and spoon and a half of sugar, again one for the mid-morning break and one for dinner. Finally I needed something in which to carry all of these items and for this Sid generously provided me with his old Army haversack.

My employers has said the job did not involve any heavy manual

233

work – though this was not strictly true – so I didn't require any special clothing such as overalls or dungarees. An old suit or odd jacket and trousers with a shirt and jersey or jumper would do.

Most of these were already available and I could continue wearing the boots that I had worn to school, but to smarten me up Sid thought I needed one additional item. This he duly produced. It was a glaringly bright, canary yellow tie. Now I was all kitted out and ready to take my place in the grown-up world.

The day before I started work – Easter Monday – was beautifully sunny and I found myself sitting alone on our front garden wall looking across an eerily silent, Hafod Square. Many families had joined the usual bank holiday pilgrimage to the beach near The Slip or perhaps Singleton Park.

I had other things on my mind.

I was starting work the following day and more than a little apprehensive. I was entering an entirely new environment and as I sat on that wall I tried to imagine the people already working there, particularly the apprentices. I had heard accounts of some nasty and horrible initiation rites and ceremonies concerning new apprentices.

Time was dragging and I was in need of some distraction from these disturbing thoughts. I needed to be somewhere which would allow me to put things into a better perspective, where I could think positively and banish the fears in my mind.

And of course I knew of just the place.

Although it was late afternoon I was soon on my way, striding purposefully towards Llewellyn Park. But it wasn't there that I would find the solitude and comforting surroundings I was seeking. I was making for the quarry – and my secret hideaway.

Before long I was scaling the quarry rock face, a much easier task now than my first attempt on the day when I had stumbled across Erica's secret hideout. I expect it wasn't as daunting because I was much taller and stronger now which helped greatly when springing from the rock face to the overhanging tree at the top – the most challenging part of the climb.

Strangely, when I stood up after reaching the top I seemed to gain courage and reassurance from the magnificent panoramic view that unfolded before me. I was looking down over Swansea and out to sea. I was completely alone at that moment but I felt an amazing inner strength, as, with arms folded and legs astride I stood there soaking in the early evening sun. My confidence seemed to come from the proud town of which I was part.

For a moment I thought of Mam, of her courage and endurance, especially in the early years of the war. I though too of my family, school friends and the good neighbours who had supported us in our times of need. I imagined the many people who, down through time, might have stood on this commanding spot before me. I seemed to gather strength from them.

This was Swansea, a special place.

This was where I belonged.